THE TROJAN HORSE

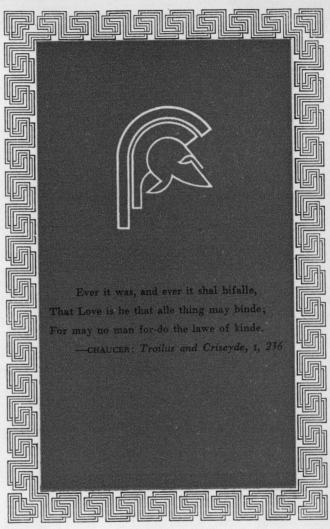

Ever it was, and ever it shal bifalle,
That Love is he that alle thing may binde;
For may no man for-do the lawe of kinde.
—CHAUCER: *Troilus and Criseyde*, I, 236

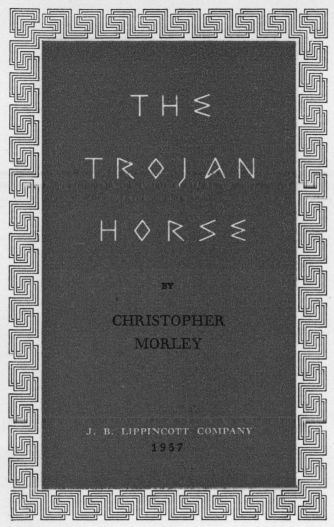

THE TROJAN HORSE

BY

CHRISTOPHER MORLEY

J. B. LIPPINCOTT COMPANY

1937

First Edition

Fowler
9.

1-30-56-JLm
3-8-56 cdm

To

G. C.

Come Back And All Will Be Forgiven

RECUYELL

OF THE

HISTORIES OF TROY

What did Troy look like?
 Nobody knows:
Still by the pasture
 Simois flows.

Troy, before fable,
 Was actual town:
Still on her rubble
 Ida looks down.

Who were her people?
 No one is sure:
Yet through the cycles
 They shall endure.

Hearts that were dusty
 Centuries gone,
Kin by conjecture—
 Gnôthi seautòn!

Priam was cautious,
　　Hector was bold;
Men were in love there,
　　Women grew old.

Purposes covert,
　　Glamor life lacked,
Show, in the hindsight,
　　Truer than fact.

Troy, become legend,
　　Is everyone's loan,
Funded to satisfy
　　Debts of our own.

What men made fertile
　　With anguish and toil,
Proves, for the poet,
　　Parable soil!

The characters are:

PRIAM, King of Troy
HECTOR, Commander of the Trojan army
PARIS, abductor of Helen
DEIPHOBUS ⎫
ANTENOR ⎪
⎬ Trojan officers
AENEAS ⎪
TROILUS ⎭
FUSCUS, a colored slave
ILIUM, the Radio Voice
DR. CALCHAS, an economic expert
PANDARUS, a financier
DARES, his butler
MISS DICTES, his secretary
SARPEDONI, proprietor of a Shore Dinner roadhouse
AGAMEMNON, the Greek commander
MENELAUS, an indignant husband
ACHILLES ⎫
AJAX ⎪
ULYSSES ⎬ Greek officers
NESTOR ⎪
DIOMEDES ⎭

) ix (

HECUBA, Queen of Troy
HELEN, "the face that launched a thousand ships"
CRESSIDA, daughter of Calchas and niece of Pandarus
ANTIGONE, her friend
CASSANDRA, Priam's daughter; a radical and pacifist
ANDROMACHE, wife of Hector
CREUSA, wife of Aeneas
LYDE, a woman reporter
　　Musicians, dancing girls, hetairai, soldiers, populace

) x (

The chapters are:

PROLOGUE.—IMAGINE, PLEASE

IT IS EARTH'S MOST FAMOUS
town, so it belongs to everybody, and to all times at
once. You must build it in your own mind. Put it on
a rocky hillside above a channel of shallowing green
water. Put over it your own favorite sky; give it
your most familiar birds and flowers, sounds and
savors. Just for a moment, concentrate on essentials:
the wide freshness of sunny air, the breath of pine
and fern and cedar, the clear blue spread of distant
sea, the snake on the stone still warm at dusk. How
many million years did it take him to counterfeit
that lichen pattern, and what is time to him?

Or to us. Were we given memory to suggest how
unimportant is time? We think a lot of Now, but
isn't Then always getting the better of it? Let's mix
them together and make Always.

Imagine, please (as though it were the opening
vistas of a moving picture) the town in long perspec-

tive. As we come in from sea, across our private ocean of doubt and delay and despair, it looks perhaps as it would have been visualized by Chaucer and Maxfield Parrish: a stylized medieval stronghold, with walls and towers and battlements. Conical turrets are washed in sunset, against the darkening lavender of Mount Ida. Dear to any city is a neighboring mountain, even if only a hill. It gives somehow a sense of solid permanence; which we terribly need.

As we look carefully, it's odd: among medieval walls and classic temples we see perpendicular modern skyscrapers, radio towers, filling stations, and a seaside roadhouse down by the beach, Sarpedoni's Shore Dinner. A concrete road, with a yellow taxi moving, runs on neutral ground, between the lines, from the city to the shore.

There is a military camp (the Greek Expeditionary Force) laid out neatly not far from the town; a flagpole flies a banner with the initials G.E.F., and below the camp the Greek fleet is drawn up on the sand. Greek officers in helmets and armor are hurrying about in little chariots, or drilling infantry. Behind a huge camouflaged screen of canvas and foliage some are building the Wooden Horse. Sentries on the walls of Troy gesture mockingly. Here and there are engagements or skirmishes—a party of Greeks bathing in the river are surprised by a Trojan sally; or Trojan foragers run from attack and take refuge inside the city.

This panorama, first seen very small and remote, comes closer. A distant murmur, growing louder, is now sounds of battle, clash of weapons, confused voices, running feet. Evidently the last scrimmage of the day is going on. There are cries, indistinct, which we might suppose to be a foreign language; but no, suddenly they come clear; so full of energy, excitement, that we never pause to think them grotesque.

Look out! Look out for Achilles!
Well stopped, Troilus!
The kid can take it.
Only a few minutes more.
Come on, gang, let's go.
Watch that double shift.

A crashing cheer, in unison of many voices: *Hoi polloi, hoi polloi, hoi polloi, Sparta!*

A cry: *A pair of horns for Menelaus!*

A derisive horn is blown twice. Louder shouts and tumult.

'At's breakin' through, Sparta!
Pretty work, Ulysses.

The voice of Agamemnon: *Short yell for Europe!* followed by another mass cheer: *What do we want? The Hellespont! Europe, Europe, Europe.*

The voice of Hector: *Inside the walls, Trojans. Shut the gate!* There is a heavy booming slam, a great door closing. A referee's whistle shrills. Complete silence.

And then an ironical Trojan voice from inside the walls: *Not tonight, Menelaus.*

II

DRESSING ROOM

W<small>E SEE THEM FIRST THROUGH</small> a kind of fog. Is it the mist of Time (which we affected to disregard), or the pale haze of Romance? In the vapor, figures are moving; we hear voices, but a peculiar steady hissing drowns the words.

The fog is simple, it is clouds of steam; the hiss, falling water in a shower bath. It's the dressing room where some Trojan warriors are cleaning up after the day's fighting. Through the fog we see their naked athletic bodies under the spray. (Naked bodies have no date; nor naked minds either). They shout to each other as gaily as college boys, or golfers at the club.

But the water turns cold; they howl. As the steam thins we see that they have dropped their antique armor in piles along the wall, under a row of pegs each marked with a name. These are Hector, Paris, Aeneas, Deiphobus, Antenor, Troilus. Their clothes (modern underwear, ancient tunic and sandals) are hanging on the other side of the room. Each tunic has its owner's name stitched on the back.

There are two long benches, and a rubbing table. Troilus, youngest of these officers, is lying face down on the table, massaged by Fuscus, a small elderly black slave. The others are shivering under the spray as the water chills. We must be allowed to interpret their conversation into a parallel argot.

ANTENOR: Snappy work today.

AENEAS: Boy, am I set for chow.

DEIPHOBUS: You got a date tonight?

PARIS: Hey, it's turning cold.

ANTENOR: *Turning* cold!

AENEAS: Ouch!

Hector is the senior warrior and commander of the regiment. He is too much a veteran to squawk about a cold shower, but he puts his head out of the spray and chaffs the coon. Fuscus has been their attendant since the siege began, and they allow him much familiarity. Fuscus, you dinge (says Hector) how d'you expect us to fight a war without hot water?

Fuscus, busy kneading and slapping, vents an endearing negro cackle. Yassuh, nosuh, Marse Hector, you-all does utilize a powerful lot. That ole boiler jest caint accommodate.— Fuscus is hoping they won't guess that he hurried Troilus, his favorite, into the bath first, to get plenty of the hot.

Troilus, from his prone position, with his head on his arms, murmurs something inaudible.— What you say, Marse Trolius? Did I land on a misery? I reckon you got a confusion on that left cheek.

I said, Troilus repeats, the Greeks don't have hot water.

No *suh*, them Greeks aint got nothin' but the ole Hygiene Sea. I reckon thass why they call theyselves Spartans.

(You can see the boy's shoulders shake a little).

The other officers have come from the bath. They towel themselves, slip into their shorts, sit on the benches to finish dressing. It is good to see them first in stark human simplicity; even the most famous heroes were once young and unconscious. But we must be careful not to prejudice ourselves toward a merely comic viewpoint.

Is anybody going out to Sarpedoni's tonight? asks Deiphobus. That shore dinner would taste good.

Lissen, Marse Phobus, says Fuscus, you be kinda niggerly with that shrimp salad. Along about fightin' time tomorrow you be libel to the gripes.

Tomorrow's a holiday, Deiphobus observes.

Better be choosy anyhow, there's other kind of shrimps down that-a-way.

Hector, who feels his responsibility, tolerates the old servant's chatter because he knows it contains much good sense. He comes to the table where Troilus is lying. How's that shoulder, he asks.

Troilus, trying to be polite—notice the respectful way he raises and turns his head while Fuscus is manhandling him—says, All right sir, I guess.

Don't try to do everything all at once, Hector advises. There'll be plenty of fighting yet.

But I've only just got into it, says the youngster. I want to do something fine.

Well, go a little slow till you get broken in.— Hector smiles (a bit grimly) at the boy's enthusiasm. He judges the handsome back and shoulders with the eye of a connoisseur; he and Fuscus exchange glances of understanding as Hector indicates the massage he wants done. The slave rubs the shoulder with oil.

This here's a beautiful muscle, Marse Trolius; what they calls a deltoid, you want to take care of it. Thass what put the ole shove behime a spear. That, an' this here trapezius—

Lay off, you're tickling, says Troilus. He gets up and goes to dress; the colored man follows him to the bench still giving a final polish to the admired anatomy. The boy listens respectfully to the conversation of his seniors.

AENEAS: The Greeks weren't so keen today.

ANTENOR: They're not so much. I had a terrible inferiority complex about them at first. I

) 8 (

thought, just because they were Europeans, we couldn't possibly match up to them.

AENEAS: Funny, that's just the way I felt.

PARIS: Europeans are so damn sure of themselves, they think they know so much more than anybody else, they get away with it just on bluff.

ANTENOR: It's the old story, Europa and the Bull.

PARIS: That time I was in Sparta, I never saw such a bunch of egotists in my life. It just made you hanker to put something across them. That was really one reason why—oh well—

The others are too gentlemanly to pursue this into personalities.

AENEAS: Still and all, I don't know, they've got something over there that we haven't got. I suppose because it's a new country, more chance for initiative. Gosh, I hope I get a chance to travel and see some of those places. I'd like to start something somewhere.

Hector, in spite of his fiery temper, does not believe in undervaluing the enemy. There's quite a few Greeks to be disposed of, he remarks, before you go sightseeing.—Deiphobus says, The Greeks have some swell fighters but they're short on team-work. —Paris, in a confident mood, suggests They're getting stale.—Canny old Fuscus, hanging up armor, can't hold in any longer.

We-all gettin' stale too, Marse Paris. Dis a mighty endurin' sort of war.—He finds a dent in Paris's breastplate.—Holy cat, someone sure give you a strong peck in de shirtfront. Dat don't look stale to me, it look timely. Yes *suh*, it look purposeful. You want to supervise yo'self.

ANTENOR: I was noticing Menelaus. He's getting a bit slow on his feet.

FUSCUS: He got de rheumatiz from sleepin' cold. I reckon even if he did break into dis town he'd be too puny for Miz' Helen.

Paris throws a wet towel at him.—Don't get fresh, you black magpie.

DEIPHOBUS: Nothing slow about Achilles. That bird is tough.

HECTOR: You say so for my instruction?

Troilus has been obscurely troubled by the tone of this conversation. But the mention of Achilles thrills his eager spirit.

I wish I could fight like that, he exclaims. There's something splendid about doing things the way he does. That straight-arm thrust of his—Zeus, what a stroke!

He imitates it with a gesture. His agile grace delights the other men, but he sees them watching and is embarrassed.

DEIPHOBUS: You parried it pretty well.

TROILUS: I didn't really parry it; I ducked it.

HECTOR: You must sidestep. That leaves him wide open, off balance. You might get into his ribs.

TROILUS: Is that fair?

HECTOR: Anything's fair against Achilles. You could have sliced him from below when you ducked under his spear.

TROILUS: I thought of that, but—I guess it's silly—his eyes were so bright. He was grand, he was so intense. So—all in one piece, so absolute, complete. I don't know how to say it, d'you know what I mean?

HECTOR: I know.

TROILUS: I kept on thinking, they're really beautiful when they're fighting.

HECTOR: It's true. Everyone's beautiful when he's doing his stuff.

DEIPHOBUS: But don't get too thoughtful about it, out on the front line.

TROILUS: I didn't know war was like this; it makes you feel clean, somehow. You don't really hate anybody.

HECTOR: Go on kid, get into your clothes. You'll catch cold.

Troilus retires to an alcove, unconsciously practising a sword-stroke as he goes.

The boy's shaping up well, says Paris.—He'll make a good soldier, Hector admits.—Unless, Deiphobus suggests, he stops to admire Achilles at the wrong moment.——There's material here for argument; Hector is on the point of saying, perhaps that's the spirit that makes the best soldier of all? But their attention is diverted. Fuscus, who has been cleaning armor and putting away weapons, drops a folded paper out of a helmet.

AENEAS: Hey, Dusky, you dropped something.

FUSCUS: Yassuh, Marse Aeneas, jes' a lil bitty paper fell outen Marse Trolius' headgear. I'll put it right back.

AENEAS: What is it?

FUSCUS: I dunno suh, I take note he alluz carries it there. I suspicion it's kind of a memorabilia.

ANTENOR: Papers in his helmet? Let's see.

FUSCUS: I was fixin' to put it back, I had a notion it was private.

Do as I say! Antenor shouts angrily. He threatens the slave. Yassuh, yassuh, Fuscus apologizes; I didn't go to be ornery.——He surrenders the paper, and the four younger warriors cluster round to examine it; but not Hector, this is beneath his dignity.

It's his schedule for the day, cries Antenor, amused.——This is good, says Aeneas. Serious minded youngster, what?——He won't take it so hard, Paris remarks, when he's been in it as long as we have.——

) 12 (

Maybe he will, says Hector: that's what I like about him.

Antenor laughs: He's got everything timetabled. Listen:—

"6 A.M., Prayers and Gymnastics. 7 A.M., Equitation. 8 to 12, Study, and Manual of Tactics. 12 to 2, Overhaul Equipment. 2 to 6, Fighting. 6 to 7, Examine Errors of the Day."

This causes a cackle, but Hector, listening moodily, suggests: That would take some of you boys longer than an hour.

Six o'clock's too early to check up, says Paris. Most of the errors come later.

What's the rest of it? asks Deiphobus.

Antenor continues. "7, Dinner. 8 to 9, Guard Duty. 9.15, Prayers and Bed."

They look at each other, somewhat aghast.

DEIPHOBUS: Don't he ever relax?

AENEAS: He'll never get to be a soldier that way.

PARIS: You can't have a decent war without some kind of social background.

HECTOR: You ought to know.

PARIS: Skip it, he's coming back.

Antenor hastily gives the paper to Fuscus, who replaces it in the helmet. As Troilus returns, fresh and shining in his clean robe or chiton, Deiphobus covers the awkward moment by saying, Tomorrow's a day off, isn't it?

Yes, Aeneas answers; there's that big patriotic service at the Palladium. You going, Troilus?

Why, we all go, don't we?

We don't have to, says Hector. The squad gets leave for the day. You can break training if you want; do you good.

Colonel, you're smooth, says Deiphobus, giving Hector a humorous salute. I'm going to take a little wimp down to the shore and give her swimming lessons.

The breast stroke, I suppose, gibes Antenor.

If you want to pick a good one, better go to the service, Aeneas suggests.—They'll all be there in their prettiest flimsies.

That's what I call patriotism, says Antenor.— Have you seen that little brownie in the yellow tunic?

Thanks, I've made my own arrangements. (Deiphobus is quite smug about it). Troilus doesn't seem much interested in the topic. His mind is still on military duty. Hector, he asks, what you said about side-stepping a straight-arm: what's the trick of timing it?

I'll show you, says Hector; look here, you. . . . At this moment a bugle is blown outside, there's a trample of feet, the clatter of grounded spears, and a deep voice: "Ho Basileus! The King!"

Cheese it! says Deiphobus: Here's Priam!

Antenor whispers to Aeneas: Here's our chance to examine the errors of the day.

King Priam enters, in classic panoply. His officers jump to attention. He fixes them with a magisterial eye, just long enough to effect the proper anxiety.

I suppose (he says) you're all pretty well pleased with yourselves. Maybe you didn't know I was watching. I never saw such an exhibition. You let that crowd of Peloponnesians push you clear up to the gate before you show what's in you. What sort of fighting is that?

They stand uneasy and abashed. It's rather like a football team savaged by an angry coach.

PRIAM: Hector!

HECTOR: Yes, sir.

PRIAM: Achilles is your opposite number. Why do you let him get past that way? He was breaking through between you and Paris whenever he felt like it.—And you, Paris!

PARIS: Yes, sir.

PRIAM: You've been in this thing from the start, you ought to know the signals by now. When the boys make interference for you, follow it.

PARIS: Yes, sir.

PRIAM: Aeneas, I saw Deiphobus take out Ajax, why didn't you smear Ulysses?

AENEAS: I wasn't good enough. He's very shifty, sir.

PRIAM: He is, eh. They're all shifty. You fellows seem to think we can soldier along with this thing indefinitely. It can't be done. The situation's serious. Antenor, cut out the grand-stand stuff. Chasing old Menelaus down the sidelines isn't getting us anywhere. Lay for someone your own metal, like that smart Diomedes, and knock him cold. The only man I saw picking out the tough eggs was Troilus, and he's not ready for it yet. Troilus, your swordsmanship's terrible. Get some vitamin. Keep your elbow loose, but throw some back behind it.

Fuscus has been nodding approval to these comments. Yassuh, King, I done tole him he muss use dat trapezius.

Priam, wise old executive, also knows how to use the lighter touch.—I'll put Fuscus out there, he says, to show some of you how to do it.

FUSCUS: Nosuh, nosuh King, I jes' figurin' the *theory* of it.

PRIAM: Soldiers, I'm not joking. There's a lot of queer things happening: you'll hear some of them on the air tonight. You've got a day off tomorrow to think things over. Pull yourselves together, and work like Trojans. Show me something on Monday.

He gives them a formal salute, which they return punctiliously and in unison. But after he has gone they slump dejectedly on the benches—except Troilus, who stands erect with eager resolve.

Dat ole Basilisk, mumbles Fuscus, he know what he talkin' about.

Troilus blurts out, We mustn't let him down.

BULLETIN

Troilus walks back to his lodgings for dinner. Though he is the King's son (one of many) he has taken rooms of his own away from the palace, to be more independent. His way goes past the office of a newspaper. In the dusk, electric letters run flickering across the cornice of the building :—

THE EVENING TROJAN . . . FIRST LAST AND BETWEEN THE LINES THE TRUTH . . . NEWS EDITORIALS FEATURES ADVERTISING . . . ONLY COMPLETE COVERAGE IN ASIA MINOR . . . SIEGE ENTERS TENTH BIG YEAR . . . HELLENES REPULSED IN SKIRMISH . . . PATRIOTIC RALLY AT PALLADIUM TOMORROW . . . PACIFIST MEETING DISPERSED BY POLICE . . . TONITE PERGAMUS PARK DANCE CARNIVAL . . . 150 PARTNERS NO INTRODUCTIONS NECESSARY FOR SOLDIERS IN UNIFORM . . . READ ADVICE TO LOVELORN ON FEATURE PAGE EVERY EVENING . . . AU-

DITED CIRCULATION 50,000 . . . FLASH . . . DOCTOR
CALCHAS PROMINENT ECONOMIC EXPERT DE-
SERTS TO ENEMY . . . SWIMMING LESSONS BY LE-
ANDER LIFEGUARD AT HELLESPONT BATH CLUB
. . . PERSONAL INSTRUCTION . . . HEAR ILIUM ON
THE AIR TONITE RADIO VOICE OF THE EVENING
TROJAN . . .

PORTRAIT OF UNCLE PAN

CRESSIDA'S APARTMENT IS SO
modernist in furnishing, so classically simple in design, it might just as well be very ancient indeed.
(The genuinely old is never incongruous; only things that are slightly old seem antiquated.) Broadcasting is lucrative: Cressida's father, the popular purveyor of ether, has employed the most expensive interior decorators. A great window and balcony overlook the street.

The girl in the room is Antigone, extremely pretty, and in spite of that Cressida's great friend; one of the very few of Cressida's own gender. She is looking at a big hour-glass which stands on an antique carved chest; there are only a few grains of sand left to run; at that moment Pandarus, Cressida's uncle, is admitted.

Pandarus, let it be noted, was the brother of Cressida's mother, not of her father who has just committed an act of scandal, in a family where there has been already too much notoriety. Small, dapper, and cynical, Uncle Pan is in semi-formal Down Town dress: striped trousers, short black coat, waistcoat with white slip, wing collar. He is not much over fifty, with a neat well-trimmed beard, and a monocle. His mind is as wary and well-trimmed as his appearance; for half a century it has been figuring things out just a little quicker than other people; but it is also capable of real kindliness.

Gracious, Pan, Antigone exclaims: Why does a banker have to look like a sexton?

We had a War Loan meeting, he says. Besides, a respectable financier should look as much as possible like a sexton, or a butler. They perform essentially the same functions for society.

(I don't know whether you notice it or not, but I detect in Uncle Pan's voice just the faintest touch of accent, of deliberated choice of words, which suggests that his family did not, originally, come from Troy.)

I was just waiting to get Ilium on the air, she says. It's almost time. She shows the hour-glass.

I don't trust those things. He consults his watch.

I can't remember whether Cressida put it on Daylight Saving, she continues.

How is she?

She seems all right. You know how she is, it's

) 21 (

always hard to tell what she's really thinking about.

Hm. Just as well, I dare say. I wonder if you know what I'm thinking about?

Probably; and she opens a compartment in the antique chest, bringing out whiskey and a siphon.

I guess you know how it works, she says. Then, touching a switch at the other end of the chest: I've turned on the radio. You listen, I'll tell Cressida you're here.

Pandarus has evidently had a difficult afternoon, for he mixes the spirit and the soda in a proportion that suggests emphatic desideration. Then he decides, looking at it, that it's too strong, and pours it untouched into a bowl of flowers. While he is splashing another and much milder highball, a bugle call comes through on the air, followed by the Radio Voice:—

This is Ilium speaking, the radio voice of the *Evening Trojan*. Well folks, tonight I've got some hot news for you. The Reverend Doctor Calchas, well known radio economist and minister of the First Broadcast Temple, has hedged all bets and gone Greek in a big way. In other words, the Doc has quit and joined the enemy. He left a statement saying that economic pressure will force Troy to give in eventually and he prefers to be on the winning side while there's time. I don't know whether the Censor will like me to say that, but the radio voice always gives inside dope without fear or favor. Doctor Calchas' departure don't worry me much, but it's tough on his beautiful daughter Miss Cressida, socialite, who remains with us, and deserves our sympathy. Me personally, I think the Doc did a nose dive at the wrong moment, for out on the battlefield today things looked upsy-daisy. Colonel Hector and his storm troops drove those Europeans back for big losses, and Lieutenant Troilus, who recently got his commission, made a brilliant debut in his baptism of fire. I guess those are mixed metaphors, friends, but I'm under pressure taking these bulletins right off the ticker. Stocks rose a couple of points on the exchange, which is a good sign, and at the War Loan meeting the tycoons were saying the bottom of the depression had been passed. With prices the way they are, away down in gamma, now's the time to buy, fix up the home, make repairs, and keep money in circulation. Advertising linage of the *Evening Trojan* is 15 per cent ahead of this month last year, though I admit the gain is mostly in the classified ads for Situations Wanted. While I'm talking to you, folks, they've handed me a slip of paper—thanks, chief, do you want to read it to them? Okay, I'll take it, just a moment till I see if I can read that script—say, this is swell, an interview with Cressida herself. She says she has every confidence in the Trojan cause, the heroism of our brave boys is sure to win. She says she'll attend the big patterotic service at the Palladium tomorrow. Folks that's the old Junior League spirit! Another thing, the pacifist meeting of Cassandra and her T.L.D. this afternoon was broken up by the police. The authorities have been too good natured with that sort of thing, I'm glad they're tightening up. You know the T.L.D. stands for Trojan Liberal Demonstration, but some of the wits are saying it really means Take it Lying Down. I could make a crack about that, but my time's up. Read the *Evening Trojan* for News, Editorials, Features, Advertisements. Okay Asia Minor, 1185 B.C. Marches On!

During this spiel Pandarus paces to and fro, drink in hand, listening attentively but unconsciously a trifle pompous. He puts his monocle in his eye as though it helps him to visualize the distant speaker. (When we get to know him better we may notice that the eyeglass is an automatic index of his mood: when he is simply sincere and human he lets it drop and forgets it.) He shows signs of approval. At the end of the broadcast he turns off the radio, finishes his highball, puts whiskey and siphon back in the cabinet. Cressida comes in.

What frightful nonsense, she says; but amused

rather than angry.——How dare they do that? I never gave any interview.

I gave it to them, my dear. Satisfactory, I think.

I suppose you know best. But really, all that patriotism and Junior League stuff, how that sort of thing bores me.

My dear, you can't afford to be bored by anything just now. Adverse publicity would be very unfortunate. If I hadn't been prompt I dare say they'd have raked up a lot of old gossip that would be annoying. Newspapers can do a great deal of mischief unless they're properly guided. As they say in their own jargon, we've got to play ball with them.

And I have to go to the Palladium stunt? I hate to be stared at. You know I haven't been going out at all.

Absolutely essential. This terrible news about your father puts us in a most difficult position. Here am I, one of the mainstays of the War Council, and my brother-in-law goes over to the enemy. My dear child, intelligent as you are, why didn't you warn me what he was going to do?

I hadn't the faintest idea. The only times Daddy was ever communicative and confidential was into the mike. If that was what he intended to do, you couldn't have stopped him.

I didn't mean that, remarks Uncle Pan, dropping his monocle.——I might have done it first. The economic situation is really impossible.

Well bless your old heart! You're really talking sense.

Yes, forgive me.——And he replaces his eyeglass.

It's all nonsense, she says; but again, not bitterly but tolerantly; her foremost quality is good-humored pliability; she instinctively follows the path of easy grade and likes to please everyone.—— The men (she continues) have even forgotten what they're fighting about. As for the women, when they see themselves in those new gas-masks of yours, they'll be horrified. Like a pack of police dogs. You ought to keep the women keen about the war if you want to make a success of it.

(It's characteristic of her, by the way, to assess the situation according to its reaction upon the sexes. The prime duplicity is by no means unknown to her; she has been perhaps oversensitized in the matter by an earlier marriage which was not a success. The details of that affair are known only to the family, but apparently its conclusion was attended with various public comment, which has made her shy of publicity in all its forms. The casual negligence of Chaucer's allusions to an eroded romance are a model of literary tact. Not to attempt to explain what we know nothing about, oh an excellent rule for narrative. Blessed Chaucer, never afraid of humanity's two great interlocking privileges, beauty and absurdity.)

I hope you don't talk to other people the way you do to me, her uncle remarks.

No one ever does, you wicked old saint.

I admit, the beautiful women won't like the masks, but there are always more of the homely ones, and it gives them an advantage. However, we mustn't be satiric. There isn't time. . . .

(With evident reluctance he abbreviates. Part of his charm is the pleasure he has in hearing himself talk. Only too often he has to be his own best audience, relishing his own precise phrasing, and its faintly corrupt overtone of mischief or malice. But he can also listen with equal attention when anyone else talks well. He is greatly tempted at this moment to boast a little about the profit he is making in selling gas-masks to the government; and some other matters too; but refrains. He has many thoughts in the back of his mind; and keeps them there, where they belong.)

The immediate point, he continues, is this: I want you to change your clothes; right away.

Don't you like this dress? I put it on because I felt I needed cheering up, and I thought you'd stay to dinner.

I like it very well; you know my susceptibilities; but it's a little too cheery. I've arranged to have a feature writer come up to do an interview with you for tomorrow's paper.

Poor fellow, he probably leads a squalid life, he'd be pleased to see somebody in a pretty dress.

It isn't a fellow, it's what I believe they call a Sobbing Sister. If she finds you looking so lovely she'll be terribly sore. It's very important to make the correct impression.

Uncle Pan, I can't, I just can't. You know I'm not clever that way.

Don't be silly. That's fine, just as you are now: that look of dismay.

You'll have to stay and help me.

Much better see her alone, so she won't think you're being coached. Just remember: distress and bewilderment over renegade parent, renewed patriotic devotion, redden the eyes a little, and if you have any knitting? A pair of socks in your hands gives time to think before you answer.

But I don't know what to wear. I didn't know I was going to have a renegade parent. . . . Would the divorce dress do? It's all out of date now, the skirt ought to be shortened.

If she's a reporter she might remember it.

You know your women, don't you. Uncle Pan, this is awful.

I think the Junior League uniform. That's neat and modest and sufficiently militarist.

I gave that up, the Sam Browne belt gave me a big bruise. Most of those Junior League girls are so flat-chested. I had it altered for Antigone.

She's not flat-chested.

You've been using your monocle, I suppose. You know, the divorce dress was rather nice.

I suppose it has pleasant associations.

It was black, austere, but quite smart; the sort of thing the judge likes and makes people feel sorry for you. It rather corresponds, in the female wardrobe, to that outfit you're wearing.

Well, I'm glad someone feels sorry for me, I've got a lot on my mind. If you think the dress'll do, get into it, and have Antigone wear the uniform. Quick now, that lady may be here any minute.

It'll make dinner very late, says Cressida as she goes. Do you think I should ask her to stay?

What are you having?

Breast of wild hen.

Too symbolic. No, I wouldn't ask her.

It's not flat-chested anyhow.

If she gets here before you're ready, I'll tell her how terrible you feel.

He is meditatively looking into the cabinet when the telephone rings, to which he replies: Oh yes. This is her uncle. Will you come right up? Apartment 6-A.

He closes the door of the cabinet.

V

IT'S REALLY IMPRESSIVE

Façade of the Palladium, the great temple of Pallas, shrine of the Trojan people. Below the pillared portico broad shallow steps descend. On one side a News Reel man is setting up his camera, on the other the Radio Voice of the *Evening Trojan* arranges his microphone.

I better try my acoustics, he says. Hey, News Reel, tell me how this sounds from over there.—He speaks into the mike, burlesquing himself.—This is the *Evening Trojan*, folks, covers Asia Minor like the plague. Your friend George Ilium trying out his beautiful acoustics.

NEWS REEL: Is it acoustics or acowstics?

RADIO VOICE: Nerts. The broadcasting office has put the ban on Greek pronunciation. Talk Trojan.—Folks the great day is here and I wish you could watch it with me. Here comes King Priam and his fifty sons, by heck; excuse me I mean by Hecuba, the First Lady, or so we assume. Queen Hecuba is wearing a muslin overall which does more than justice to her royal stature—Lyde, where are you?

NEWS REEL: There's that cockney accent again.

RADIO VOICE: No it isn't, I don't mean Lady, I mean Lyde, Lyde the fashion reporter, she was to be here to help me describe the dresses.

NEWS REEL: She's doing a rush for the early edition.

RADIO VOICE: Then I'm sunk. I feel terrible today anyhow, we had a party down at Sarpedoni's last night. (He is adjusting the volume control, and these sentences come out with a terrific roar.) The whole crowd went off the deep end, I'll tell the world.

NEWS REEL: Evidently.

The populace is gathering; Ilium ducks behind one of the massive pillars to fortify himself with a slug from a flask, and then becomes professional:—

This is the Radio Voice of the *Evening Trojan,* speaking from the Palladium, historic temple of Pallas. Folks the great day is here and O boy O boy what a scene. I wish you could watch it with me, we've set up the mike right here on the portico of the temple and already the crowd is coming in. There never was such a turnout, it looks to me as though half the city is pouring into the square. It's as though they're all coming on purpose to show that in spite of some recent surprises we're not discouraged. It's regular Trojan weather, I never saw a sky so blue, the air is like wine. That reminds me, while I don't intend to annoy you with commercials I must just say that this is exactly the weather to have a look at the *Evening Trojan's* seaside bungalow development out at Saline Shores. Admission to the property by showing one of the coupons printed in the paper, and when you see what a dandy little homesite can be had for just a few drachmas down payment, well, all details in today's *Evening Trojan*.

The crowd is coming in faster and faster, orderly and in perfect silence. You know the old legend, this is the day sacred to the goddess, Pallas, the goddess of wisdom, protector of the Trojan state, and if everyone keeps silence the goddess herself will speak. Behind me in the temple her great image is surrounded with fresh flowers, the children of the city were up before dawn today gathering them on the slopes of Mount Ida. Of course admission to the temple is restricted to the clergy, high officers, ministers of state and the royal family, the rest of us remain respectfully outside and observe absolute silence. This is the first time one of these ceremonies has ever been broadcast and believe me the *Evening Trojan* had plenty difficulty persuading the high priests to let it be put on the air. I should like to add

) 32 (

that though the goddess only speaks in moments of great national crisis, your favorite newspaper speaks every afternoon in News, Editorials, Features, Advertisements.

Now folks, they've opened a lane and the procession is coming through. It's really impressive, it's wonderful, I don't know how to describe it to you, it makes you realize how we all feel about this great city of ours. Some of the women are crying. Here's King Priam, I can see King Priam! I can see that splendid beard of his winding slowly round the throng. He's walking by Hecuba, our beloved Queen, and he's completely surrounded by a bodyguard of his sons. I don't know what it is, there's sort of a divinity about a king that really gets you, the crowd knows that silence is the rule but you can always trust our Trojan folks to know what to do, they make motions of applause without actually making a sound.

The King is walking up the steps of the temple. He and his officers are in full armor, it's really wonderful, we don't forget that though this is a day of armistice we are still engaged in a great war, certainly a sight like this brings out all one's patterotic emotions. It's certainly significant to think that we Trojans worship the goddess of wisdom and all those Greeks seem to worship is that big wooden horse they're building out there, think of it folks, making an idol out of a perfidious horse, certainly that's a sign of a crude civilization. It begins to look as though the Greek culture and Greek art and all that sort of thing had really been overrated.

King Priam and his bodyguard have halted at the top of the steps, they look over the crowd in dignified silence while the rest of the procession take their proper places. Folks this is really impressive, I don't know whether I can get any of it across to you, but honestly I could almost reach out and touch the King where he sits. The crowd has found its own way of expressing its feelings and still not break the silence, you can see ripples of approval, excitement, as their favorites come up to the steps and make their bow before approaching the temple. Here's Paris and Lady Helen, my she's beautiful, I wish you could see her like I do, she's wearing a blue sort of a robe and the Greek fillet in her hair, you don't realize until you see her in the full sunlight that her hair has a red light in it, I don't mean a traffic light folks, I mean a lovely sort of bronze shimmer. When you think of all the trouble she started it's surprising she's so popular, but it's the kind of trouble lots of us would like to have more of. She and Paris both get a wonderful reception, you can see it in people's faces. I think everyone respects Paris for being so persevering about keeping her here in Troy. Naturally the world's most beautiful woman would gravitate to the world's most beautiful city.

It's really wonderful the way this has all been worked out, there isn't a hitch anywhere, the soldiers are lined up on one side of the steps and the Junior League girls on the other, the girls are all in their natty uniforms and they certainly look slick with those Sam Browne belts and little doughboy caps, all standing just as serious and determined looking and so wonderfully reverent, I guess it's sort of symbolic of our Trojan idea of sex equality and giving women a share of citizenship, I believe we're a lot ahead of the rest of the world in that sort of thing. Look, I mean listen, here's something interesting, this is unusual, the crowd shows its interest, speaking of sex equality here are young Lieutenant Troilus and his sister Cassandra walking together, you know they're twins, remember they used to call them the Priamese Twins, I'm sorry folks that's terrible. It's interesting, two identical twins and such different ideas, Troilus is quite the military hero he just got his baptism of fire as I told you last night, and his sister Cassandra is leader of the T.L.D. that is making all these pacifist movements, it just shows to go, I mean goes to show, what a real democracy we have here in Troy, all parties can get together when it's a question of the national welfare, it's really impressive. Troilus looks tremendously handsome and very serious, he goes on up the steps, Cassandra is very pale, I guess she doesn't approve of so much military display, but really it gets you. There are a lot of big shots coming in now, the members of the aristocracy who have seats reserved in the temple, oh here's something that certainly gives me a kick, here's Lord Pandarus the banker, you know how popular he is, they say he's really the power behind the finance ministry, he never takes office but he's the one who really pulls the strings, and with him is his lovely niece Cressida. That's wonderful of him, because Cressida has been on the spot, her father Doctor Calchas deserted to the enemy, and naturally people resented it, you can just see that her uncle wanted to give her his confidence and support by walking with her. Folks this is really dramatic, and you can see the crowd realizes it, Cressida is wearing black, the only woman wearing black in this whole crowd, it's as if she's wearing mourning for what her father did. Say, she certainly has class, it's wonderful how that black becomes her, her face is sort of aloof but she certainly carries her head high, she doesn't seem to look at any one, you can see she's been through an ordeal and she certainly has the crowd's sympathy, it took courage to come here like this.

Wait a minute, I think something's happening that wasn't on the program. Wait a minute, folks, till I get the hang of this. King Priam is making a signal—well, say, for heaven's sake, it's a gas mask drill. I heard there was going to be a surprise and this is it. Certainly it's an amazing sight, honestly it's incredible. Wait a minute, get this, I'll try to tell you what happened. King Priam held up his hand and at that moment everyone here, all the troops and officials, and the Junior League, put on a gas mask. I wish you could see them, it's unbelievable, it's simply colossal. They've just handed me a slip of paper, it says to tell you this demonstration was secretly arranged by the high command to impress the public with the absolute solidarity of our will to win. Of course we had heard that the enemy were going to use gas but I had no idea our preparations for it were so complete. The crowd is simply thrilled. Stand by now, the King is making signals again, everyone is absolutely still, wearing those weird-looking masks. The high priest, Dr. Laocoon, holds up his arms, it's the gesture for the silence, for the goddess to speak. I can only whisper, quiet everybody, stand by . . . the royal family and the priests go inside the temple to kneel before the goddess . . . the silence is omnious.

(A protracted hush. Then the Radio Voice continues in an awed whisper).

Could you hear that? There was a voice, a cry. I believe the goddess did say something. . . . Wait a moment, something queer's happening. There was a scream. Say, Colonel, can you see what's going on? The public's waiting to hear. . . . Just a moment, folks, stand by, I'll take care of you. . . . Nothing like this ever happened before, everybody's flabbergasted. In the middle of the silence Cassandra shouted something, the priests tried to stop her, it's a terrible thing to do. She broke away, she's run out here on the steps, she's haranguing the crowd and a whole flock of T.L.D. plàcards have appeared. It's another of those pacifist demonstrations. The King and the priests don't dare leave the presence of the goddess, the guards are trying to quiet her, she goes on irregardless. Zeusalmighty what a story! Wait a minute folks, I'll drag the mike over, see if we can catch what she says. You're certainly listening in on a unique event; excuse me brother I've got to get this mike over there; you're getting all this by courtesy of the *Evening Trojan*, News, Editorials, Features, Advertisements, read your newspaper for full details. . . . Please, miss, put it here where the radio audience can get it. . . .

CASSANDRA: She will not speak. The goddess will not speak. Do you expect Wisdom to reply to your folly? Is her temple a kennel, to profane it with the faces of dogs? Look at yourselves, look! Hideous and absurd, like grinning beasts, turning Wisdom's people to a pack of hounds to yap and slaver and destroy; turning beauty's world to madness. I warn you, Wisdom has fled this place. Animals, muzzled animals, answer me if you can.

RADIO VOICE: Folks she's right, it's extraordinary, they've all got the masks on, they can't speak, they can only make a sort of growling gobbling noise, really it does sound like a pack of dogs. Wait till I turn the mike so you can catch it. That shrill yapping is the girls in uniform, they're furious, they're trying to tear their masks off so they can answer her. Gosh, this is a terrible sacrilege! I can see our News Reel man working like mad to get pictures but I bet the censor never passes them. The T.L.D. banners are waving applause but all the others can do is growl. Now Dr. Laocoon and the priests have come out, they've got Cassandra under control but the crowd is milling around on the steps. I guess she's right, the goddess of Wisdom is out of town for the day. Here comes the King, folks it's King Priam himself, I wish you could see the look on his face, he's holding up his hand for silence. They say that means me too. Signing off, this is the *Evening*—

(One of the priests must have pulled him away from the mike).

VI

ON THE RAMP

AFTER A GOOD MANY YEARS OF fighting, Greeks and Trojans have reached, by mutual attrition, some sensible compromises. Both high commands realize that if the enthusiasm of the troops is to be maintained the war must be kept reasonable. Accordingly, combat in the field is usually concluded by 6 P.M., and hostilities of all sorts given a positive curfew at 9 P.M. A strip of territory running from the city down to Sarpedoni's Beach has been declared neutral, and is frequented during the evening hours by soldiers of both sides. They meet there in the pursuit of relaxation, as we shall have a chance to observe presently. Their attitudes are not cordial, but at any rate without open breach.

In Troy itself, the walk along the ramparts is the favorite evening promenade. It commands a broad view of the whole terrain. From the battlements we see the two rivers (Scamander and Simois) lined with clumps of willow and shimmering ranks of reeds; and lotus lilies in the backwaters. Far out in a sea suffused with late sunset is the blue outline of Tenedos Island. On the landward side, the pointed conifers of Mount Ida silhouette in fringe against pellucid twilight.

From below, inside the wall, rises the hum and movement of the city at its evening affairs. Outward, we look down on the Greek camp preparing supper. The wall is not open to civilians until the 9 o'clock signal, for occasional arrows, rocks, fireballs or ingenious stinkpots are likely to come over.

Troilus, in full fighting kit, is on guard duty on the wall. Fuscus, with a little pushcart, comes down the line collecting the armor of his troop. I'll take yo' stuff, Marse Trolius, it's right on closin' time.

Troilus, peering into the twilight, waves him away. Wait a minute, he says. I'm trying to figure out what they're doing down there.

Which way, dat bonfire down by the river? I reckon dat's Menelaus, it look like he makin' a smoke barrage of his ole socks. Poor ole Basilisk, He mus' be pretty desperate.

No, no; there by the cypress tree.—Then Troilus's voice changes. Look out! Low Bridge! he cries sharply, and Fuscus crouches behind the battlements. There is a nasty whizz, and Troilus, holding up his great shield, catches an arrow on it. He waves ironically at the enemy and answering catcalls are heard from far away. He holds the shield for Fuscus to pull out the missile. Then he sees that it has a paper folded round the shaft.

Another one of those messages. Read it.

Who, me? I don't read any such trash. What it say, Marse Trolius?

Troilus smooths out the paper; the slave produces a flashlight by which the message is read. "Trojans, why prolong the agony? Economic Forces doom you to defeat."

For goodness' sake, cries Fuscus, what-all way is dat to fight a war, wid economics?

I'll bet that was Diomedes, says Troilus angrily. I think I can still get him. See if I don't make him jump.

He picks up his sling, inserts a stone, and aims with great care. As he is doing so the 9-o'clock siren sounds.

Cheese it, Marse Trolius, dat's curfew.—But Troilus has gone too far to restrain. He lets fly, and apparently scores a hit, for there is a yell of pain, followed by a multiple shout of anger.

Nicked him, says Troilus.

Dass good slingin', but you get in trouble dat-a-way, shootin' after hours.

Troilus seems absent-minded. He gazes moodily

over the wall as Fuscus removes the armor and piles it in the cart.

It seem to me nobody obey de rules any more, dis ole war gettin' out o' control. Dey's gettin' to be too many undercurrents to suit my taste. Too many undercurrents, stream go crazy an' flow uphill.

Troilus, leaning against the rampart, pays no attention.

Take dat big Greek Horse, fer instance. I wish I knowed what dey tryin' to abretize. Take dem scan'lous doin's at de big jubilee an' de way Miss Cassie act up. What-all a war comin' to if its own lady folks take a scunner on it? Lawzee, don' we fight dis whole shootin-match to do credit to a lady?

Still, to the darky's disappointment, his master keeps silence.

Those Greeks, they don' look to have no genteel behavior for ladies. You can tell by de way dey carries on with dem Hittite an' Sanskrip floozies down at the beach. Look how dey wanted to keep Miz' Helen cooped up in dat ole Lacydemon wid no chance to make a reputation for hersef. Dis war, ef it don' fizzle out, goin' make her reputable for a long whiles to come. Lissen honey, widout dey's fightin and ructions, what future has ladies got? You can't have high-class trouble without a lady to smarten it up, no more'n a spaniel can't eat without gettin' his ears in de gravy.

One of those big three-quarter moons is rising over the sea; the moon at its phase when it looks most human. Softly it is getting the better of the sunset aftershine. Perhaps Troilus was waiting for the evening to grow a little darker before saying anything; but Fuscus' innocent babble would lure confidences from the Sphinx (the only creature more delicately reticent than a sensitive young man).

Suppose, Troilus says; and pauses.——Suppose you haven't even met the lady you want to fight for. I mean you've seen her, but you hardly even remember her face.

FUSCUS: Maybe dat's lucky.——Excuse to me, Marse Trolius, I don't mean it the way it sound.—— Thass what they call co'tly love. It's de bes' kind. ——Among de quality, love aint got no call to get too pussonal.

TROILUS: Don't you think, if a face is beautiful, you ought to be able to think of it in detail? If you were trying to remember a face, what feature would you think of first?

FUSCUS: You gotto remember, Marse Trolius, if I'm thinkin' about a face, it's a different kind of a face.

TROILUS: All I can really see is the eyebrows.

FUSCUS: That's a pretty feature, I used to

take note on 'em mysef. It always strike me queer, those lil bitty hairs to grow jes so, it's cute, they mus' be some sense to it.

TROILUS: Glorious! I'd like to bite them.— Do you suppose anyone ever did?

FUSCUS: Well now, does you mean some special eyebrows, Marse Trolius, or eyebrows as you might say in bulk?

TROILUS: It was just a crazy thought. People don't do silly things like that.

FUSCUS: Nosuh, no indeedy. (But he can't control himself; the rich infectious negro laugh rings out. He smothers it, however.) 'Pears to me like I better push on and swage de rest of dat armor. —But as he leaves, Fuscus adds: Marse Trolius, I'm proned ter believe, most everything bitable has already been bit.

What the coon says is probably so, but it doesn't bother Troilus who is already thinking his own thoughts. We pass, if you please, into quite a different mood. Rare indeed the young man who, if left alone under adequate stimulus, has not experienced it:—

The forward moon that hurried early up
Wasted herself against such gaudy light,
Unnoticeable; and then suddenly,

Swift as the gust that crimps a windward water
Competing colors doused, and there she rode
The singular of the sky.
So did that lady shine above the crowd:
In all that great assembly only she.
My eyes stood to, like awkward raw recruits
To make their shy salutes—
Salutes, recruits, there germinates a verse.
Zeus, isn't it wonderful just to talk to yourself!

I am well served for making shallow mock
Of friends who showed an interest in girls.
I had a boy's plain curiosity
How are they made, and why;
But wearied of the ribald tedious jape
Of trull and flittermouse and catchmequick,
And so, the young dogmatic, I announced
Life was full already, without women!
That a face could satisfy the heart
And pledge the nerves in such convivial wine,
Rising like health, like sap through every twig,
To ramify and foliate the mind
And be so simply right—why I, I, I
Just had no notion!
O sweetheart, in that shameful temple brawl
She simply raised her brows and looked apart.
Regardless of all clamor and dispute

Just arched her brows, and looked don't-give-
a-damn!

What color were the eyes? What have they
seen?
What has she thought about? and would she
tell?
What does she look like when she sits at home?
Where was she all this while? Unperfect health?
Or waiting one accomplished to arouse her?
How does she speak in her loquacities,
What sound of voice? I guess a trifle shrill
With some confidential tones of mischief.
How dress her hair? Has lots of pretty garb
To keep the eye expectant of devices?
How shaped indeed to please a closer eye?
On this side fulness, surely, yet of heft
Sufficient to afford a lively wrestle.
Farce, I belabor the unknowable!

But just the way she stood, the very poise
And turning sweet contrivance of her body,
The flux from one to other attitude
Was motion absolute; unconscious, pure.
And yet a sense so cunningly conveyed
Of damns she did not give, must still have been
At least a tinge, a tithe, considerate art?
She arched her brows and didn't seem to look—

No, no; *she* didn't arch them, they were shaped
Upward by nature, like delicious bridges
For idle thoughts (like these) to cross, to pause,
Look down, and watch themselves. . . .

Thus the glorious unconscious lunacy of a boy
thinking romance for the first time; just letting it
roll. But one does not remain long solitary on the
ramps of Troy in a night of stainless moon. Antenor,
Deiphobus and Aeneas, in summer flannels and each
with a light-o'-love on his arm, come by the bastion.
They are amused to find Troilus there; it is contrary
to his schedule.

ANTENOR: Hi! How come? You're off duty.

DEIPHOBUS: Still checking up the Errors of
the Day?

AENEAS: What's the matter with Prayers and
Bed?

TROILUS: Don't let me interrupt you.

DEIPHOBUS: Come on with us, we're going
over to the Square. Sour Puss is at it again.

TROILUS: I don't think I understand.

DEIPHOBUS: Cassandra's holding an open
forum, questions and answers on public policy.

ANTENOR: We've got some questions to ask
her.

AENEAS: We're taking the girls along to il-
lustrate.

(The young ladies laugh merrily to show that they too enjoy the joke. Troilus is puzzled but still polite.)

TROILUS: Very nice, I'm sure.

DEIPHOBUS: We're going to ask her, if Troy's going to fall anyway, why shouldn't these girls do it first?

(Troilus is disgusted. He remarks with dignity : I have a touch of fever, gentlemen; I pray you pardon me.)

ANTENOR: Hay fever.

AENEAS: He's not very sociable. Don't come too close : Mayonnaise is dressing.

DEIPHOBUS: Maybe we can find Paris. He'll go with us.

ANTENOR: I saw him going into a pub.

TROILUS: (As he leaves) More likely you saw him *coming*.

VII

A TOUCH OF FEVER

Pandarus, knocking at the door
of Troilus's lodging, gets no answer, but hears a female voice in utterance within. Making cautious
entry, he is amused to find Troilus asleep on the
couch, while his sister Cassandra's anxiety issues ve-
hemently from a small radio.

It is a plainly furnished room of the Third Floor
Back sort. Pandarus looks round: not inquisitively
but with swift observant scrutiny. He notes sheets of
scattered scribble on the desk where the young man
has been trying some verses; large photos of King
Priam and Queen Hecuba on the bureau; a shield
and spear in a corner. He sits in the only easy chair,
listening to Cassandra's broadcast which is now in
peroration :——

You thought it just our anthill Troy besieged?
Nay, by dire foreknowledge of the gods:

It is all kindness, decency, and wit,
All consecutive effort of man's will,
Learnings, laughters, loves, and life itself
Here held in leaguer—

(*The voice is drowned out by ironical applause,
laughter, shouts, catcalls*)

. . . Machines and sciences that master man
Until the human face, our only guess
What gods may look like, sweats in shame,
Lurks in a jackal jowl. And Superbeast
Publicity, hyena bitch with wings,
The harlot, strumpet, vampire, succuba,
Summer in loins and winter in the brains,
Cohabits and canoodles drowsy souls
Rots the skull with intellectual pus,
And makes us carrion!

(*Uproar, cries of shame and protest, come over
the air. Pandarus shows signs of shock, is about to
turn off the radio, but changes his mind and listens
further*).

I didn't say Carry On (*continues Cassandra's voice,
    with quite insulting calm*) I said Carrion.
I was a nice child once, spoke well-bred speech,
Until The Wisdom seared my tongue with coal

And forced me cry these cindered words upon you.
By her decree, I give you utter choice:
Open your gates to foes and let them come,
Bid them in as travelers on picnic
Eager for shows and curiosities,
And take good profit of them. So, outsmart
Their childish temper, and refuse to fight.
So, cut the cord umbilical of hell.
Or else? They come, as otherwise they must,
In conquest and in spiky wreaths of fire
And lo a hundred generations yet
Men sift our ashes, sneezing in dispute
Where stood the sullen walls of silly Troy.

(*We hear an uproar of rage and dissension*)

I told the Vice President in charge of Production
They wouldn't listen. . . .

(*And now, with beautiful contemptuous irony*) :—

Civilization, roll your one good ear
Deep in the goosedown pillow:
Go to sleep!

Exactly what he did, says Pandarus, clicking off the radio switch. I'm glad he didn't hear it; he'd have been terribly shocked. I wish the Left wasn't always so sinister. Some day the Popular Front will get a kick in the behind.

Troilus, who had been sleeping peacefully to the drone of the broadcast, wakes, and grumbles drowsily: Who turned off the radio, I was listening. . . . Oh, hullo Pan, I'm sorry, I guess I fell asleep.

My boy, says Pandarus (he's very fond of the young man) I haven't seen you in ages. I heard you'd been sick.

I've been a bit off color for several days, Troilus admits.—I guess I've got a touch of fever.

You're lucky. Think of still being able to get feverish about anything. That's the sad thing about my time of life: everything is so tepid.

Nonsense, you old hypocrite! I don't know anyone who gets as much fun out of things as you do.

Oh, but it's such temperate fun. I don't like these malignant pervasions of equanimity.

Troilus is a little anxious whether his manuscript verses have been observed; looks toward the desk to see if they're all right.—Have you been here long? he asks.

Just came in. I was listening to Cassandra on your radio. I think she's got fever too.

Those outbursts of hers are very embarrassing. She calls them boring from within.

Boring is right. These radicals are so dreadfully

sentimental. They talk about the Rape of Helen, say why don't we give her back and end the War? Poor Helen was only a pretext, a sort of bright-colored recruiting poster for both sides. It's really a matter of who's to control the Black Sea commerce.

There must be more to it than that, says Troilus sadly. I hate to have it all seem so sordid.

Don't let me depress you. What with the income tax, the military situation, food rationing, and no angostura available for an oldfashioned cocktail, I've been a bit jaded.

Poor old boy! I guess you tycoons do rather get it in the neck.

We get it where Prometheus got the eagle; right in the liver. Well, as Ho Basileus always says, what we need is morale. But I can't take my morale straight. I like it morale and soda.

I wish I had something here to offer you. You see, I'm in training.

Nonsense; I was only joking. You know, I rather wanted to bring you a little present of some sort, but I didn't know what you'd like. Is there anything you need?

As a matter of fact, Troilus admits bashfully, there *is* something, but I don't suppose—

Now don't be pigheaded; tell me! Is it anything I can get?

Well, I think I've heard—don't laugh—is there really such a thing as a rhyming dictionary?

Yes, there is.

Marvellous! Tells you what rhymes to use to make a good poem?

Not quite that; but it can be useful. I tell you what, I'll lend you my old copy.

Do you mean to say—

Surely! I used to write verse myself. I wish I could remember some of it, I'd recite it for you.

I never would have guessed, Troilus says in amazement. (And of course the absolute quality of being young is never to suspect that anyone else was ever like that).

Ah my boy, be glad of all those fresh new senses, cries Pandarus. Savoring things for the first time: everything prime, unique, glamorous, unprecedented! Quick as a grasshopper's knee, keen as a hound's nose! That's the time to run like a dog and inhale the flavors of the world!

Maybe you'd like to look at some of my attempts, Troilus suggests.

Thanks, says Pandarus, but I got just a glimpse as I came in. I'll wait till you get them finished. A little on the gloomy side, aren't they?

Poetry does have a way of going doleful on you.

Well, don't let it interfere with your work. I noticed you weren't quite up to form on the battlefield the other day. You mustn't mind my saying this, old boy; you're our first string reserve, and we need you badly.

Troilus feels it only honorable, now, to confess to his old friend. I know I've been in terrible shape, he says. I really have been sick. You see, I'm in love.

Splendid! Who is she?

I can't tell you.

My dear fellow, I'm discretion personified. Also, I'm unshockable. I suppose it's some young person from the wrong end of town.

No.

Whoever it is, cajoles the genial satyr, I'm sure something can be arranged—if you'll remember your family position and be sensible.

If I tell you, you may be offended.

Why should I?

The only time I saw her, she was with you.

With me!—Pandarus is really aghast: all sorts of possibilities run wildly through his mind: and he thinks he has been so prudent.—With *me?* Zeusalmighty, where?

At the Palladium. The girl in black—

But that's my niece, Cressida. . . .

Your niece! That exquisite creature? I beg your pardon; I mean, I had no idea—I never saw her before.

She's been keeping to herself. There was some

trouble—it's rather complicated. The family simply couldn't have another scandal.

Would it be possible for me to worship her from a distance?

That sort of thing's unhealthy. Dear me, another problem. You haven't told anyone?

Of course not.

Perhaps I *had* better have a look at those poems.

Oh, *would* you? cries Troilus delighted. They'll tell you so much better than I can, he says, hurrying to choose some papers.—This one, for instance! He reads a few lines:—

> See how the little twisted tasselled pine
> On crank support and naked maintenance
> Spiles itself into the heedless cliff:
> So holds my love upon your rocky heart
> And roots as idiot firm!

PANDARUS: Bravo! Very pretty, very pretty indeed. Why, my boy, that has a most graceful feeling. I'm not sure the simile's apt: I don't think Cressida's heart can really be described as petrified: but it's good lyrical strategy. Certainly you shall have that rhyming dictionary.

TROILUS: I'd never want anybody to know who wrote it.—Do you think she'd like it?

PANDARUS: My dear boy, they always like

verse that's written specially for them. I don't suppose you remember the old Duchess of Hellespont; delicious creature. She was so tickled with a little thing I wrote for her, oh ages ago, let me see if I can recall it: let me see: My heart . . . my heart is like a skipping stone . . . yes:——

> My heart is like a flattened stone
> Flung gaily from the shore:
> With hope and skill so deftly thrown
> It skims the water o'er.
> Like miracle, once more, once more,
> It skips and skitters past,
> But . . . rumpty tum . . . as I deplore
> It always sinks at last.

Gracious, you make me feel young again. Well, well: so you think you really love her?

TROILUS: Oh, if I thought she'd even consent to be aware that I exist—

PANDARUS: She will. But mind you, the circumstances are peculiar. We've got to be careful.—— Yes, these verses seem to have the right touch: a very pleasant mixture of prone and supine.

TROILUS: I wouldn't even expect to meet her. If I could just wear her favor; be her champion; write poems about her—

PANDARUS: Don't ever hesitate to speak

favorably of female beauty. They may know it already, but confirmation is always welcome.

TROILUS: Girls never interested me before. They talk such rot. But as soon as I saw *her*, so different from the others—so humble and proud, and modest, to dress herself in that plain black—

PANDARUS: Hmm. Yes. Let me take one or two of these poems with me, I'd like to read them more carefully.—When do you go back to duty?

TROILUS: Tomorrow. Right away, if you want; I feel so much better.

PANDARUS: I suppose it's really a patriotic duty to keep the army in good spirits. When you go out to work tomorrow, can you vary your itinerary?

TROILUS: Surely.

PANDARUS: Instead of going down the Boulevard, take your troop through Epsilon Street. And throw a little swank into it. I'll see that Cressida is looking out to watch you go by. What time would that be?

TROILUS: Right after lunch—a few minutes before two o'clock.

PANDARUS: Good. And be sure to look your best. Chin up, chest out, plenty of spit and polish.

TROILUS: I shall be terribly nervous.

PANDARUS: Witch hazel! Faint heart never won fair lady—By Jove, that's a good line, that's worth remembering.

TROILUS: But where does she live? Will *I* see *her?* How will I know if she's looking?

PANDARUS: You go ahead and mangle some Greeks. Leave the rest to me.

TROILUS: Pan, you've got me in such a state, you devil—

PANDARUS: It's a touch of fever. I must look up my old notebooks and get those verses right—

We skim the level water o'er
And keep afloat once more, once more,
But . . . rumpty tum . . . as I deplore
We always sink at last!

VIII

DICHOTOMY

I'VE EATEN, THANKS, SAYS UNCLE
Pan (complete with monocle) as he takes a chair in
the apartment on Epsilon Street; where Cressida and
Antigone are just finishing lunch.——I had my
crackers and milk at the office. Well, my dear, I
think I may say we had a good press. The interview
with Miss Lyde has had a very satisfactory effect.

Definitely, Cressida says; perhaps with a little
whiff of irony. Pandarus cocks his eye at her watch-
fully. He does not always know quite how to take
her.

Your dignified behavior, he continues, was all
the more favorably noticed by contrast with Princess
Cassandra's deplorable outburst.

Since you've come just at lunch time, I suppose
you're looking for a snort.

Just a trivial one, he agrees. He doesn't really

want it, but he sees she is in a captious mood, and thinks it may help.

We're glad of an excuse, says Antigone as she makes the necessary preparations. What a morning!

How do you mean?

All the sacred cows have been calling, Antigone explains. Queen Hecuba, Lady Helen, Andromache, Creusa. They came to congratulate us on our patriotism.

PANDARUS: Excellent. That shows the power of the press.

CRESSIDA: They all brought their knitting and settled down for a good palaver.

ANTIGONE: If the Greeks can be beaten by gossip, they're certainly licked.

CRESSIDA: It was rather embarrassing, we didn't have any knitting that looked at all patriotic.

ANTIGONE: I was working on a girdle, I had to try to turn it into a muffler.

CRESSIDA: Women ought not to do so much knitting; it gives them double chins.

PANDARUS: It's looking down all the time. They should look up.

CRESSIDA: At a man, I suppose.

ANTIGONE: They get double chins on their minds too.

PANDARUS: Yes, it's terrible what life does to women.

CRESSIDA: You've been noticing it for years, haven't you.

Pandarus realizes that he's not going to get anywhere on the line of banter, so he wisely takes a drink instead. Cressida and Antigone suspect that this is his way of conceding the first round, so they feel better too. The three lift a silent toast to each other, the underlying sentiment of which, whether expressed or divined, is "To hell with Sparta."

I admit the patriotic ladies must have been rather trying, says Uncle Pan. But they're useful as a social backstop.

They're so gruesomely earnest, poor dears, murmurs Cressida. They've got prickly heat about the affront to the goddess of Wisdom. They say she's gone over to the Greeks, the way Daddy did.

It's not impossible, Pandarus admits. But remember we still have Aphrodite on our side. Generally speaking, I think she's more useful than Pallas.

You're just arguing from your own experience, says Antigone.

I'm sorry you're both so flippant. (Pandarus is just a trifle peevish.) What I'm trying to tell you, Cressida, I think you should get out more. You need social diversion. You don't want to be an introvert.

How do you know we don't? What is it?

People who stay at home and think about them-

) 63 (

selves until they get morbid. It always makes one feel better to get out and compare yourself with other people.

That's all right for domineering creatures like you, Uncle Pan. I just don't feel gregarious.

Well, it's too bad. I suppose I made a mistake. But I can still cancel the order.

What do you mean?

Get Madame Iris on the phone, I'll countermand it before it's too late.

Madame Iris, they exclaim! The dressmaker?

I'm afraid it was a liberty, he says. I told her to come up and take your order for some new clothes; as a present from me.

Pan, you darling! You old rogue, what are you up to now? You know you ought not to do that sort of thing.

We'll take it out of the War Chest. It's strictly a military measure. It's not good for morale to have the two prettiest girls in Troy shut themselves up like nuns.

Darling (Antigone to Cressida) did you notice, they're wearing a new kind of tunic, with a smooth shoulder: I saw one at the Palladium.

And the highlow waist, finished off with a peplum!

In Persian rose, and a yoke at the hip!

It seems a pity to cancel it, he says, pretending

to reach for the telephone. Quietly but firmly they push him back to his seat.

When's she coming up?

Some time this afternoon. I told her not until after the parade. The street will be so crowded.

Parade, here?

Yes, didn't you know? The Boulevard's torn up, so the troops will go by here on their way to the field. There's a big push scheduled this afternoon.

Poor fellows, I wish we could do something for them.

Give them a wave from the window. That's better than knitting those horrible socks.

Uncle Pan refreshes his drink. At last he feels he has the conversation under control.

You know, he says, we not only got a good press on our Palladium appearance, but we made a conquest. Quite a remarkable one; a young man of considerable importance. He saw you at the service and was completely smitten.

I'm not interested.—How do you know?

He told me so.

Wasn't that rather indiscreet?

I'm afraid I wormed it out of him. He didn't mean to tell, but he was in such a state he didn't realize what he was saying. It was quite pathetic because he's never had anything to do with women before.

That's what we need, more men like that.

Of course I shall respect his confidence.

Quite right.—Who is he?

He's written some poetry about it, really quite unusual. He gave me some of his manuscripts to look over.

Uncle Pan slyly takes the papers from his pocket and glances at them. I'm glad the arts keep alive in war-time, he says. Yes, some of this is excellent. It's a pity it's too personal to be published.

Did you want us to criticize them for you?

Why my dear child, he protests, I wouldn't dream of violating a pledge. You see, they have his name on them. But I'll read you one, if you like. This one is less emotional, more in the humorous vein.

And, assuring himself of their close attention, he reads :—

I saw no merit in the scheme
   Of Nature's primitive division :
Though sex, they told me, was supreme,
   I held it always in suspicion :
      It seemed too gross, too much imbued
      With propagative purpose crude!

But now, O palinode, confess :
   Dichotomy proves more appealing,

For since I saw you, loveliness,
   I have a wholly different feeling:
      To my astonishment intense,
      Biology makes better sense.

Magnificent is Nature's plan,
   Provocative, ingenious very,
To make a woman and a man
   So mutually necessary:
      Let Beauty flourish her allures—
      I am, appetitively yours. . . .

CRESSIDA: There are a lot of words there I don't understand. What's dichotomy?

PANDARUS: Hm, well, it's a philosophical term. I wonder if I can put it so you'd understand it.

CRESSIDA: If that's what it is, better not.

PANDARUS: No, no; he only means the fundamental antithesis of gender.

ANTIGONE: How philosophers love to beat around the bush.

CRESSIDA: I bet you wrote it yourself.

PANDARUS: Absolutely not; cross my heart.

CRESSIDA: Whoever wrote it, he has a sense of humor.

PANDARUS: That's only a defence mechanism to conceal how deeply he feels. In the other poems he lets himself go.

CRESSIDA: They always do, sooner or later.
I wish we knew Uncle Pan's retort to this; but
their talk is broken by the sound of a bugle, marching feet approaching, and a ruffle of drums. Here
come the soldiers, Antigone cries, and they hurry to
the window. Uncle Pan is very zealous, motioning
the girls forward so they can see. Antigone needs no
urging, she waves a scarf and shrills with enthusiasm; Cressida, more reserved, holds herself a little
backward. Splendid, splendid, says Pandarus; you're
going to get a fine view. By Jove, a smart-looking
lot, aren't they? A military band, breaking into the
full blare of the Trojan anthem right in front of the
house, drowns his further comment, but we can see
him gesticulating and shouting in Cressida's ear.
As with most of those past the age of front-line
service, military music gives him an ecstasy of
fervor. Cressida, to her uncle's dismay, seems rather
grave, even a little saddened by the spectacle.

Look, look, he cries as the band fades off; there's
Hector, he's the head of the whole regiment, the
best soldier we've got. He's been through it all right;
you can see it in his face. He's the only man who
can really stand up to Achilles. Yea, Hector!—And
his shout is caught up and reverberated by the
crowd in the street below.

They say he's been wounded in seventeen places,
Uncle Pan says with awe.

Goodness, says Antigone pertly, I didn't know men *had* so many places. Hurray, Hector!

Uncle Pan ignores the cheek. There's Aeneas, he points. A man with a future, he'll be heard from one of these days. The son of old Counsellor Anchises, you know. A good fighter. Yea Aeneas!

And Paris! I guess you know *him* by sight! He has an air to him, hasn't he; see how he always wears his helmet tilted, it looks rakish. I think myself he does it because his hair's going a bit gray on one side. He's earned it, I bet. A man who acts as judge in a beauty contest is just hunting for trouble.

Who are these two honey-bears, laughing and talking together? asks the impressionable Antigone.

A couple of bad boys, says Uncle Pan. Those are Deiphobus and Antenor. Grand fighters, and afraid of nothing, but if one of them takes off his hat to you on a dark night, call the Travelers' Aid.

They're popular though, says Antigone. Listen to the cheer they're getting. I *like* them, they look like sweet potatoes. Hullo, you bad boys, she shouts. Her words, perhaps fortunately, are lost in the noise of the populace outside, but both officers recognize something amenable in the timbre of the cry, and identify its origin. They look up; Deiphobus salutes with a wide grin, Antenor carries farther still with a slow lingering wink. Young Antigone burns a clear flush of surprise. Cressida feels the instinctive hackles of sex pringle up her nape. She knows—or remembers—that old insidious come-on stare, the fighting taunt of another enemy.

Uncle Pan, leaning far out to watch the army flow by, does not notice. He never supposes himself to miss anything, but this he does not see. How can he guess it is partly Cressida's reaction against the brute impudence of that look that makes her sensitive to something so different a moment later? He is studying the moving lines, a river of bronze with floating plumes, and lustred with sun on spearpoints. He cries out in a different tone :—

Here he comes! Here's the boy I cheer for! The youngest officer in the regiment, and going to be the best in the whole army. Only got his commission last week, and look how he sits that horse! That's a soldier for you. He's been sick too, but he's going out for duty just the same. Hurray, hurray, attaboy Troilus!

The cheer is re-echoed by the crowd with such vigor that Troilus himself is startled and looks up. He has taken off his helmet in the heat, and there is boyish grace on the clear brow and head of damp curls. The face, a little thinned by recent grievance, is brownly pale; then, as he sees Pandarus, darkened by quick blood. He recognizes Cressida, standing behind her uncle; sees her oblivious to the nudging chatter; meets her steady curious gaze. Slowly his face drains of color, there comes upon him an unconscious intentness. It is as if he strives to memorize something he may never see again; or gropes in mind for a rhyme that does not exist. It is as if he is fallen asleep as he rides, and the moment a dream, prolonged and unchangeable for ever.

Troubling and yet serene, the appeal of such unmarred quality in a boy, when perceived by ripened woman. It pierces to her earthbound necessity, her kindness both protective and passionate; stirs the bitter sweetness of all energies unused. She is barely older than he, but aware beyond her years.

Still he wonders, searches her with eyes. In sudden uncalculated impulse, in warm pity and astonishment (few women ever meet so honorable and unselfish a look) Cressida seizes flowers from a bowl at hand, and flings them out. Moving in trance, he leans far and catches them. But one falls; the horse shies and stumbles; the rider braces to tighten reins, and canters forward. The troop breaks rank a moment, closes up, passes on; he does not look back.

Who was that boy, she asks.

Pandarus is amazed. Didn't you hear me shouting? That's Prince Troilus, that's the one—I mean, that's the one's got more stuff in him than all the rest. Priam's youngest son. Believe me, there's a boy that's a born soldier.

She is watching down the street, where the sunburned men are turning a corner. A pair of shoulders, still identified, stiffen and square themselves; releasing a mood, preparing for decisions.

What a pity, she says. How lovely they are, it's a shame to see them wasted.

Her uncle is a little puzzled, and offers no answer. He makes his adieu promptly; says he must get back to the office.

(She is not good at accounting for herself; even to herself. It would not even occur to her to try. Yet I wish she and Uncle Pan might have been alone together, just then, for a little while. Pandarus, with all his mischief, is always glad to lay aside chaff; he is easy to tell things to. O, when the moment arrives to confess, how often is the right confessor there also?)

Well! (says Antigone when Pan is gone). A lot of excitement for Epsilon Street! Do you suppose they'll march by here every day?

Cressida does not seem to be supposing anything.

I better clear away lunch, Antigone goes on. The dressmaker may get here. Darling, think of having some swell clothes. We've been old maids in lavender such a long time. Are we lavender or are we lysol? It *would* be nice to fascinate somebody again. Wouldn't it?

Maybe, says Cressida slowly. . . . If you can do

it without being fascinated back. . . . Hand me the dictionary.

Antigone does. Cressida looks something up; from the part of the dictionary she opens it might be "dichotomy."

Antigone continues gaily:—

Let's get all tinselled up and go to Sarpedoni's. I'm fed up hearing about Man in the Abstract. I'd like to see a few actual samples. . . . Say, look: Pan forgot his friend's poems, he's left them here on the table. I suppose it wouldn't be right to look at them?

She starts to unroll the papers.

Give them to me, says Cressida quickly. I'll take care of them.

IX

SARPEDONI'S

An ENJOYABLE PLACE IS SAR-pedoni's after a day in the field. Done with heavy armor and hot scrimmage we can run down to the beach by taxi from Troy; or there's a private bus waiting outside the Greek camp for the use of the Spartans. A cool splash in the lilac-tinged surf of sunset, and then in clean slacks and blazer stroll up to the bar. Time, probably, for a couple of quick ones before the girls arrive; and a little chat on the incidents of the day, with the enemy politely ignoring you at the other end of the counter. (The cash register, which plays no favorites, is exactly in the middle). Sarpedoni, immense Turk, his broad swarthy face shining with perspiration and shrewdness, asks if you want an alcove reserved for quiet susurrus; or would you prefer to sit out closer to the floor? And presently the Myrmidon Boys will mount their little orchestra stage, amusingly built cymbiform like a classic galley. The melting grievance of saxophone and tortoise-shell mingles with the easy lapsing rhythm of the mild Aegean Sea.

Sarpedoni, acquisitive Asiatic (Old Soapy, the boys call him) has taken every precaution to be neutral, and to see that both sides are given equal opportunity for pleasure. A white line is painted straight across the premises, exactly dividing bar, dining room, dance floor and terrace; it even continues across the beach to the bath-houses. Like all institutions of human service, the place has grown up gradually to meet a specific necessity, and Greeks and Trojans alike have been rigorous to observe a tacitly adopted code of behavior. Both, on their own sides of the formal equator, enjoy the relaxations which make war endurable. Perhaps, since the Greeks are far from home and have no city to return to, the proprietor favors them a little : at their end of the bar, for instance, is the famous Lonelyhearts bulletin board and Personal Mail Desk. Here, with prudent pseudonymity, Greek warriors in quest of consolation can post Personals and appoint exploratory rendezvous with the Hittite *marraines* and Sanskrit chippendales of whom Sarpedoni has a reservoir on tap. It was on Sarpedoni's advertising board that Agamemnon and Achilles first got in touch with those two nymphs Chryseis and Briseis who caused so much trouble, as Homer (though discreetly) has intimated. If Homer had not been blind, he would not have been surprised at the Chryseis-Briseis episode.

Several officers are already at the Greek end of the bar. Perhaps we can judge their temperaments by what they order. They seem to fall into three pairs. Agamemnon and Menelaus, who are feeling the strain of such prolonged campaign, take gin and tonic. Ulysses and old Nestor share a pitcher of beer, which they spin out through the whole evening; Ulysses with a stub pencil is sketching for the old man his ideas about the wooden horse. Diomedes and Ajax, who always go first to the bulletin board, clink a planters' punch.

Here's a pathetic outcry, says Ajax. He reads from the Personals:—

ENGINEER OFFICER, Aryan, 3 years overseas, austerity finally broken down, needs congenial companion. Bathing, hiking, beach sports, cultured conversation. Off duty afternoons, Mon., Wed., Fri. CAPTAIN SAPPER.

A sap, all right, says Diomedes. He won't get much of a nibble on that. I'm more interested in the other side of the board. How do you like this one:—

Boy friend invalided home, acceptable locum tenens welcome. On the buxom side, jolly pal, good dancer. Non commissioned ranks preferred; no pantywaists apply. TURKISH DELIGHT, Box 15.

That's the stuff to give the troops, Ajax admits. I must tell my top sergeant, he's the boy for her.

Sarpedoni will have to get a bigger board, says Diomedes. The warm weather's bringing 'em out in swarms. What do you suppose this means:—

REJUVENATION guaranteed. Results permanent. Send stamped envelope. CALYPSO, R.F.D. Ogygia.

You should worry! chuckles Ajax. Let's not brood about that sort of thing for a while.

Here's a nifty, exclaims Diomedes:—

HULLO SOLDIER! Tired of war? Spend your leave at Furlough Farm on picturesque uninhibited island. Stags only. Special week-end rates. Home cooking, pork products a specialty: chitterlings, fresh gammon, country sausage, hog jowl and greens. CIRCE.

Ajax suggests, It don't sound kosher.

Those ads are all hooey, remarks the unsuspecting Ulysses.

Not a bit of it, Captain, interposes Hybla, the pretty little clerk at the mail desk. All paid insertions. You ought to see the number of answers they get.

DIOMEDES: It certainly puts *you* in a strategic position, eh honeybunch?

HYBLA: Even the Trojans have been over to look at them.

DIOMEDES: Well blast their nerve. They've been getting beyond themselves.

AJAX: You said it. What did you think about young Troilus conking somebody after curfew the other night?

DIOMEDES: What did *I* think about it? I was the one that got conked. Pretty nearly fractured my skull. Believe me, I'm going to get square with that palooka.

AJAX: He's not a palooka, though. He's the best bet they've had since Hector was a pup.

ULYSSES: Now Achilles is back in it, things'll be different.

DIOMEDES: I hope so. What about that big hush-hush of yours, the mystic horse? I wish you'd—

NESTOR: Quiet. Not here. (He gestures toward the Trojans who are gathering on the other side).

AJAX: What was irking Achilles? Seemed

) 78 (

poor dope to me, beefing in his tent while we were out taking it.

DIOMEDES: Husbands' complaint.

ULYSSES: A little tact, please. (He indicates Menelaus, who is absorbed in argument with Agamemnon).

DIOMEDES: Well, call it monogamy trouble. The General horned in on his girl.

NESTOR: Briseis, one of the Chryseis-Briseis twins. A cunning little trick.

AJAX: Loud cheers, oldtimer; I was afraid you were past noticing that sort of thing.

ULYSSES: I thought everybody knew. Agamemnon had one twin and Achilles the other.

AJAX: Well, what did it matter? You couldn't tell 'em apart.

DIOMEDES: Achilles said he had a way of knowing.

ULYSSES: It was another of those dirty tricks that Pallas Athene pulled on us. She sent the girls along just to make mischief.

DIOMEDES: Dr. Calchas gave us a blackboard talk about things last night. He says we've had a raw deal from the gods all the way through, but we're round the corner now—

NESTOR (he crosses his fingers and taps the wood of the bar): Please, please. No talk about the gods. It's very bad luck.

Sarpedoni, who has been making himself agreeable to the Trojans, now visits the Greek side and bows respectfully, glistening with salesmanship and suavity. Is everything all right, General? Have you ordered dinner? The snails are fresh from the mud.

Agamemnon is a little cross this evening. No snails, thanks. They remind me too much of my staff.

Sarpedoni, the old soap, laughs with the General but manages to fan the other officers with a placating sweep of his large innkeeping eyes.

The General always has his little joke. It's been a warm day, not good for hurry. Would you like the private room, I can send in some punkahs?

No girls tonight, says Agamemnon irritably. Sarpedoni waves away the misunderstanding amiably. He has the lowest coefficient of friction in the Near East. The General would like to sit out here, watch the dancing?

Anywhere, anywhere, Agamemnon grumbles. Not too close to the orchestra.—With one flash of the eye Sarpedoni has already started a waiter preparing a table, with another signalled the bartender to serve a complimentary round of drinks.—A prophylactic on the house, General, while they get your table ready.

I mustn't be a dog in the manger, the commander relents; he probably sees Diomedes and Ajax looking wistfully toward the screen where various ladies in warm-weather tiffanies emerge from the gyneceum.—Send round some janes for the others to look over. Maybe King Menelaus?

Nothing doing, I want my wife, Menelaus maintains stoutly.

If we could only find somebody to satisfy him, says the General, we could call off the war and go home.

Oh I hope not, the landlord protests. It'd be a pity to quit now; I've just made plans for a new grill room.

Send some around if you wish, Menelaus says resignedly; but I know they won't click.

Sarpedoni is apologetic. I've tried almost everything: odalisques, hetairai, concubines, paramours, but we don't seem to find the wave-length. It's certainly a tribute to your good lady.

An idée fixe, says Agamemnon.

I don't think we have any of those. But I've got a nice little team of Bosphorettes coming in.

How's the enemy tonight?

In very good spirits, General. Quite a number of parties coming down from town.

Well I hope they'll behave themselves. I'm not in any mood for nonsense.—And pointedly ignoring the Trojans a few feet away, the Greeks take their seats. Perhaps the prophylactic, or the attentions of the proprietor, have quickened the two leaders; for we notice that the table has been laid with an empty place adjoining each warrior; and a little later these seats are all decoratively occupied.

If this were your first visit you would think the evening passing in its usual good cheer. But Sarpedoni, never amblyopic, observes an undercurrent of bad humor. Even the waiters feel a subtle tension of nerves: the kitchen blackboard where breakage is scored shows an unusual number of entries. The warm evening has brought out a large attendance. On the Trojan side of the house we recognize several familiars. Aeneas has brought down his conscientious Creusa, who doesn't get out often; they are sitting over the Special Pelagian Plate in a kindly domestic mood. Aeneas, very much on his good behavior, tries to avert his mind from the halloo in the adjoining booth where Deiphobus and Antenor are a bit loud with a couple of bright-colored hinnies. Sarpedoni is annoyed to recognize that these are no other than Chryseis and Briseis themselves, who were supposed long since (after the quarrel in the Greek camp) to have gone back to their father's country rectory. He hopes old Agamemnon won't see them, but realizes that of course he will. Soapy whispers to the bar-man to water down the ambrosia cocktails going in rapid sequence to that alcove; but the strategy is tardy. Already Deiphobus has lured the girls into a promising argument whether the daughters of a parson are naturally more full of devilment than others. Because, he says, they have inherited all their sire's accumulated repressions; which must be, Antenor suggests hopefully, almost uncontrollable. The girls, by no means sotto voce, are confirming the theory. They are naively reporting some ill-chosen humors of their stay in the Greek quarters. Perhaps the polyphloisboian din prevents these reminiscent chirps from reaching General Agamemnon across the floor. But Sarpedoni shoots at the General's Sanskrit soubrettes a bugeyed flicker that means, Give him the works.

Paris, canny enough not to bring Helen here, has strolled in; carefully inconspicuous. He is surprised to find Troilus alone in a corner. The boy is in a dreamy mood; not ill-humored but pensive, content to take cover under the surrounding racket; it creates a muffling shell of exterior distraction beneath which he can speculate in secret. They sit together, drinking gently (Troilus takes only lemon squash) and talking little. From outdoors, where on each side of the restaurant an open-air garden is reserved for the troops, come gusts of impromptu singing. It's unlucky, Sarpedoni thinks (as he retires to the kitchen to put on a fresh collar) that the Trojan doughboys have chosen this evening to revive one of the more scurrilous of their choruses. Irritably he hears the rolling harmony, augmented with clanking mugs—

> A lady lives in Pergamus
>> In sin, sin, sin:
>
> Her husband made an awful fuss
>> And took it on the chin.
>> Let the fun begin,
>> The best man win,
>> Tuck up your tunic
>> With a safety pin!
>> SO-o-o-o-o
>
> Bang the gates and ring the bells
>> We don't give a damn—
>
> You'd better quit the Dardanelles
>> And scram, scram, scram.

Fortunately the Greeks on the other side are making uproar of their own. But the proprietor makes sure that the emergency sign is ready to be hoisted if necessary. This is a neatly lettered card to be run up above the orchestra stage, where (with the house lights suddenly darkened) a spot can pick it out. Its legend, he reflects, is hardly peremptory enough. It says:—

LADIES AND GENTLEMEN, PLEASE!
The Continuance of Our License
Depends on the Preservation
Of Order and Good Feeling
On Both Sides of the House
Appreciatively Yours,
SARPEDONI'S, Inc.

Until tonight, this has always worked in moments of excess. But now, measuring the subtle surcharge of social static, he does not feel sure. He hurries the Bosphorettes onto the floor for a pony ballet number.

Apollo, god of spotlights and stage managers, radiant demiurge of all dramatic mischief, may have plotted the inevitable entrance. The Bosphorettes have at last followed offstage their successively rejected garments. Applause, but not very hearty; the astute Sarpedoni has already in his mind cut their routine by four minutes. Lights up, and a small ripple of chatter, but suddenly and oddly hushed.

Even without that briefest pause, so rapidly covered by renewed palaver mostly female, Paris would have known something is happening. Troilus, inattentively considering the antics of the chorus (with their grievous madrigal about "Sarpedoni is the Boss For Us"), transmutes all this gallimaufry to some pattern of his own. But suddenly he stiffens

) 85 (

and draws back. Paris turns to look. Delayed by the prinking of new dresses, Cressida and Antigone, escorted by Uncle Pan, have just arrived. The alcoves are filled, they are given a table at the very edge of the dance floor. Beauty so exquisitely and completely clothed gives its sure delight after the prolonged skirmish of bifurcated meat. One silent pulse of astonishment—acutely mixed of admiration and envy—runs through the place. Sarpedoni, who adores pretty women, dramatizes his convoy of the trio to their table and the dexterous removal of glittering wraps. He thinks (innocently enough, as probably Apollo intends him to think) that this will provide a lucky distraction against gathering moods.

Pandarus with beaming monocle graciously glances about, saluting friends; but sits with his back toward Troilus, whom he does not see. Little Antigone frankly gapes at the complicated scene. Cressida, enjoying to the very core of her molecular femininity this first social escapade in so long, keeps her attention completely for the table and her companions. Quite genuine timidity gives a superb projection of high breeding and disregard.

Diomedes, beyond the white line, has already forgotten his three broad gambits in Sanskrit. He looks as anode must at cathode, or lion tamer at fresh lion.

Now the music is on again, lights are dimmed, partners take the floor. The white stripe across the shiny wood is a reminder, not an actual frontier; couples from both sides use the whole area for gyration; but the accepted etiquette is that both Greeks and Trojans, even in the turn or tangency of the dance, disregard each other and make no attempt to mix.

Boy, that's a pair of lulus old Pandarus has with him. (It's Paris speaking, craning out from their corner alcove). That must be Cressida, isn't it? I'm glad she's back in circulation, she hasn't been around in ages. Maybe she'll give me a whirl. Somebody's got to butt in: Pan can't dance with them both.

Troilus, keeping well back on the settee, watches Paris approach Pan's table, make his bows with courtly ease, draw up an extra chair and start a triple jugglery of conversation. An expert practitioner! He sits just long enough for manners and then accompanies Cressida to the dancing. That planished space, symbolic of the slippery poise of the whole occasion, is a pretty show, spangled now in shifting stains of colored light poured from above. In the jumbled hazards of rotation the weaving pairs approach and reverse, gracefully veer and pass, asymptote and recede. At the successive cusps of an irregular epicycloid swings agile old Pandarus, gallantly duetting with Antigone. Deiphobus and An-

tenor twirl Chryseis-Briseis through the latest tur-
bines of choreography : just enough elixir has per-
colated their ankles to foster an admirable brio.
Aeneas and Creusa are consciously decorous. The
bronzed faces of the Greeks, with their fierce and
glossy horse-chestnut eyes, are also seen above Sanskrit coiffures which show signs of rumple. Menelaus, plodding but not hopeful, is marching a sol-
dierly pattern with some Turkish doxy. Agamemnon,
whose shanks are a bit haggard, is sitting it out with
Diomedes. Both are neglecting their roxanas to
study the dancing. The General notes Chryseis-
Briseis in the stringent clasp of Deiphobus-Antenor,
and has his own reasons for remembering them sev-
erally. As the old canteen joke has it, he knows bitch
from t'other. Diomedes, who looks dangerous, follows Paris and Cressida with his gaze. The muted
glucose melody moves this human ocean in a smooth
surface swing; but underneath, little corals of anger
build and build.

Troilus watches too. He is happy to see Paris
pay deference to Cressida. Not for anything would
he himself wish to be introduced here, in this mud-
dle of noise and color. He is glad with looking, humble to confirm his revelation. Never does woman
seem so exquisite to her lover as when she dances
with someone else. He measures her loveliness as he
could never know it were he closer. Cressida, with

her great gift of doing one thing at a time, is surrendered to float and pause; creating the very rhythm she seems to follow. She says little; even Paris is less glib than usual. In a luminous web of star-colored fabric she holds the wide surplus of the dress lifted to one wrist. So slender in that broad fan of stuff, her light and tender drift is like a yacht in lazy sail, like a butterfly's idle wing. Given completely to the moment, treading on sheens of broken color, you might think her someone from Elsewhere, ignorant of our clumsy language and our barren ways. But wise beyond any warrant of experience Troilus now guesses her not goddess unapproachable. She is human woman; desirable and desired. And all round that prismed center the will to live, creation's only integral, sharpens, brightens, focusses more close.

When nerves are trimmed so tight, almost any casualty will serve. The specialty of the menu tonight is Sarpedoni's famed Chicken with Noodles, which many of the guests have been enjoying. But Deiphobus, in alcohol's unfortunate habit of insisting on an accidental jape, has found something continuously amusing in this phrase. He and Antenor, in the final eddy of the dance, are slowed up alongside the table where Agamemnon and Diomedes are glowering with one abandoned Sanskrit forgotten between them. Deiphobus, in the worst of taste and judgment, thinks it funny to ejaculate to his friend, *Chicken with Noodles*. Which the Greeks not unnaturally regard as a personal comment.

The sequel to this appears at the next dance number. Diomedes does the unheard-of. When the music begins he strides briskly across the floor, bows curtly to Pandarus, and ignoring Cressida claims a dance from Antigone. This guileless wench, who indeed scarcely knows Greek from Trojan, is swept onto the floor before she realizes what is happening. So astonished, or indignant, are all others that the two have the space to themselves. The Greeks, with a roar of applause, shout "Exhibition Number!" The orchestra plays brillianty and Diomedes, a magnificent performer, spins the girl into a tango with strong emphasis on all its sinuous and pantomime elements. Antigone, lissom little piece, enters vividly into the spirit of the thing; the skill and speed of their movement are so infectious that even on the Trojan side there is scattered clapping.

But this breach of custom is too flagrant to be overlooked. A murmur of growling protest rises from the Trojan tables. Several armed men appear on the Greek wing of the terrace, in answer to some signal from their General. As the dance ends Diomedes, with a graceful obeisance to the flushed and flattered Antigone, walks back with her to her chair.

There is a moment's threatening hush, then the Greeks shout for an encore.

But Troilus, whose head is cooler than most, sees what Diomedes intends. The dance with Antigone was only a subterfuge, an insolent preliminary, intended to impress Cressida. The Spartan bully, hot with success, will now ask the latter to dance with him, counting on her reluctance to cause a scene.

Paris, standing rigid with anger, accepts Antigone from Diomedes with a stiff nod. Old Pandarus, rising from his chair, monocle pathetically swinging, is too bewildered for initiative. There is a general movement forward from the Greek side, as though the enemy, jaded with Sanskrit, are all about to seek Trojan partners. Sarpedoni, in alarm, and thinking music the best remedy, hurries the band into action.

Things move fast. In the very instant that Diomedes begins to salute Cressida, Troilus has come up from behind. As though Diomedes does not exist, he takes Pandarus firmly and pushes him at Cressida. Your dance I think, he says quietly; and Cressida finds herself rising to take her uncle's arm, while her eyes are caught by this boy with pale brown face and metal eyes. Dance with her, you fool! he whispers fiercely in Pan's ear. This, he knows, is the only recourse. With Pandarus, a civilian and an older man, she will be safe from insult. Paris, coming to his senses, takes Antigone forward. The two couples move out on the floor; Diomedes and Troilus are left face to face.

That dance was taken, says Troilus, quivering a little with anger, but holding himself in. You know the rules here.

Oh really? Diomedes retorts. When did you get so scrupulous?

The Trojans don't use women as weapons.

I suppose you were afraid to let her make her own choice. Some of her family seem to prefer Sparta.

I think you'd better go back to your own side.

Diomedes laughs. She'll dance with me yet.

They might well have been at blows, but now they are surrounded by a knot of angry men from both armies, including some Greek hoplites with spears. Some are holding back the two, others arguing and threatening. There is a clatter of weapons. The music stops, couples who had begun to dance move uncertainly to the far end of the floor. With the clang of a bell the emergency sign goes up and is flooded with light.

Gentlemen, gentlemen! Sarpedoni cries. Please, I ask you, remember our license! Please gentlemen, no roughhouse!

Hellenes, to order! shouts Agamemnon. I demand an apology for insults.

Of course, General, naturally. (Sarpedoni tries tactfully to wave people back to their places). Ladies and gentlemen, please everybody, only take your seats, everything will be all right, just a little misunderstanding. I apologize to everybody, it's an innkeeper's business. I'm an expert at apologizing. A little quiet please, I order free drinks for the house. Give your orders to the waiters. George, take the orders.

Back to your places, boys, before he changes his mind! This from Ulysses brings a laugh and the tension is eased.

If there's any more disturbance, roars Agamemnon, I shall declare the evening truce at an end. We'll have war twenty-four hours a day.

No, General, no, pleads Sarpedoni. That won't be necessary. Thank you gentlemen, thank you for your consideration. Please, if you will just remember, life won't be nearly so amusing if you are on military duty all night.

Muttering, bristling at each other, the men on both sides draw back, ladies and escorts return to their tables, the floor empties. But Troilus strides out into the lighted space.

One moment, he calls. There is a quality in his voice that compels attention. In his hand he holds a long bronze spear.

I think *I* owe an apology; for the honor of Troy.

The mistake I made the other evening was unintentional; an accident; I'm sorry.

A curious pause, with a low murmur of surprise; perhaps of anger on the Trojan side for this humiliation.

But here's another mistake, he cries fiercely. Perhaps not so accidental. Someone dropped a Greek spear on this side of the room.

He holds it out before him, seeming to weigh and balance it with professional interest.

You might like to have it back, he says. Someone might need it.

With a glorious gesture of disdain he bends the weapon into a curve, exerts a passion of strength, and while everyone watches in amazement rounds it roughly into a circle, the point fitting into the hollow end of the shaft.

Go and roll your hoops where they belong, he says, and trundles it across the floor. It wavers, and falls by Diomedes.

The roar of the Trojans shakes the roof. By the time Old Soapy gets the house quiet again, and Uncle Pan has a chance to look for Troilus, the boy is gone.

X

MEMORANDUM

Y OU DON'T THINK I MADE A FOOL of myself?

My dear fellow, I never saw anything so superb. (Uncle Pan unconsciously removes his monocle, to visualize better in memory.) You kept your head when everyone else was hysterical. I admit frankly, I myself hadn't sized up the situation. (He puts the monocle in again, for reassurance.)

What did *she* think about it?

She didn't say much. I think she blames herself: says it was her vanity caused all the trouble.

That's absurd. It was my fault the Greeks were so sore to begin with.

It was Deiphobus' fault for getting tight.

It was Diomedes' fault for dancing with Antigone.

If it comes to that, it was my fault for buying the girls new dresses.

I suppose everything is always everybody's fault, says Troilus impatiently.

My boy, you never said truer word. A very sound doctrine.

Rather cowardly, isn't it?

Well, well, let's not argue. I was only trying to express my gratitude for getting us out of a nasty situation. If you want to know what Cressida thinks about it, you'd better get it from herself.

I think it's better to forget it.

I still can't understand why we didn't know you were there.

I was keeping out of sight; on purpose.

Well, you can't go on like that. I'm planning a big dinner-party for Cressida, to reintroduce her to society. I want you to come.

Oh gosh, Pan—I don't want to meet her in a crowd.

People who can twist spears in circles don't need to be so timid.

When I meet her I want to have a chance to talk to her.

You'll have plenty of chance. I'll let you sit next to her.

I hate swell parties. All the big shots there, that sort of thing's paralyzing.

Big shots—I detest the phrase—are only small shots who have kept on shooting. If you insist, though I say it reluctantly, I'm a big shot myself.

The kind I mean have a much noisier backfire.

You haven't heard me in the War Council.—
Well, I tell you: come and have tea with me first,
and I'll ask her too. Then you can get to know each
other.—But when you come to the dinner you must
pretend you're meeting her for the first time. I'm
not going to start any gossip.—Now I must get
along; I'm busy.

Wait a minute, says Troilus, after a moment's
thought. Maybe it would be better to meet her in a
crowd after all. You can sort of pick up ideas when
you hear a lot of people jabbering.

Come and have tea, and we'll see what happens.

Hold on, you can't go yet. Let me think this out.
What would I talk about?

You've got a phobia. Buck up! You'll talk about
whatever she wants you to. Women are trained to
take care of that.

But I'd be absolutely tongue-tied.

What, a man who can write poetry like you?

That's different. People write poetry just for
themselves. That's why it's fun: it's so absolutely
private. Nobody in the world knows about my stuff
but you.

Hm. Yes. Quite so. Well, old boy, my nose is
itching for the grindstone.

Honestly, Pan, if you don't help me I can't
come. I *won't* come.

What do you mean? Do you expect me to dictate a conversation for you?

Grand. Just the thing. Give me an outline and I'll work it up.

All right, we'll make it simple. Just five points, and you can use your five fingers to remember them.

(Troilus is delighted, and takes paper and stylus to make notes.)

First, says Pandarus, well, let's begin with something personal and complimentary. Say something nice about her clothes. She's got them rather on her mind just now. Not too sudden or obvious, but give the idea you've been thinking about them.

True enough; I have. Okay. First, something about clothes.

Second, why not ask about her amusements. Has she been reading anything, working at her music, playing games, seeing pictures? That might start something.

Second, amusements, Troilus notes.

Third, politics. That's timely enough now; but you might go a bit gently until you find out what she thinks. Fourth, if you find yourself in trouble, the campaign. And Fifth, if you need a Fifth, be confidential about yourself. Probably she'll have got you onto that long before. They're good that way. I remember the old Duchess of Hellespont—

It looks awfully scanty, says Troilus doubtfully.

Well, I'll think about it. He checks the points on the fingers of his left hand. Clothes, amusements, politics, campaign, self. I'll save the little finger for self.

Good. Don't do anything silly, and I'll phone you.

Pandarus is gone. Troilus looks at his memorandum, shows a sudden revulsion, crumples and throws it down in disgust:—

My beautiful, my beautiful, must I know you?
Why can't I just have you to myself, in dreams?

XI

THE TEA GROWS COLD

IN THE BEAUTIFUL INNER PATIO of Uncle Pan's luxurious home, what looks at first like a fountain is really a water-clock (clepsydra). Beyond the peristyle is a glimpse of blue flowers in the garden. Uncle Pan is fussing over preparations for tea. He dodges among the pillars with a fly-swatter of antique and ornamental shape. Finally he lands the insect.

Got him!

He looks over the table; rearranges flowers and doilies; nibbles a salted almond. Dares, a perfect specimen of bulky and dignified British butler, with mutton-chop whiskers and a B.B.C. accent, but draped in classic robes, rolls in cakes and sandwiches on a Graeco-Roman tea-wagon (like a small chariot or curricle).

Pan swats another.

Flies very bad today, Dares.

Yes, sir. I rather fancy it's all those 'Ellenes outside.

How do you mean?

Well sir, the Greeks always strike me as rather succulent people. A bit gamy in flavor, sir; just the sort of thing to attract vermin.

Contact! cries Pandarus, making another successful stroke.——Flies or Hellenes, it gives a sense of accomplishment when you actually smite them.—— He hands the implement to Dares; polishes and replaces his monocle; sits at ease.——But there really should be some more effective method of demuscation.

You know, sir (observes Dares) I've wondered whether something might not be done in the way of a minutely reticulated mesh; an interstitial screen of thin fabric and very fine gauge. If you see what I mean, sir: transfusible for atmosphere but exclusive of parasites. I should add, sir, of course it would necessarily extend over the entire periphery of the apartment.

By Jove, that's a good idea. Excellent. It sounds practical. There might even be money in it. If this war ever ends, we could put it on the market. Well, more urgent matters impend. Bring in tea as soon as the ladies arrive.

Very good, sir. Here's the evening paper, sir.

Thank you. That reminds me, turn on the radio as you go. It's about time for Ilium.

Certainly, sir. I must warn you, the fountain is a trifle slow, sir. I've sent for the plumber.

As Pandarus lights a cigar and glances at the paper, the Radio Voice crescendoes from within. It is just becoming audible as Cressida and Antigone arrive. Uncle Pan greets them cordially, but in dumb show; ushering them to their seats with a gesture which indicates that he wishes to hear what the radio is saying, and presumes that they do also. When we catch the words they are:—

". . . in the public interest, was not unduly publicized on account of the important personalities involved. However, the incident at a well-known beach resort was followed at once by increased activity on the part of the enemy. The Greeks have pushed their attacks very fiercely, and not always in accordance with the rules of civilized warfare. I am sorry to have to report that today they were successful in taking several Trojan prisoners, including the gallant Captain Antenor; against whom, it is said, General Agamemnon and King Menelaus had a personal grudge. This regrettable event was achieved by a clever ambush, in which our men were outnumbered and surprised. It goes without saying that it was resisted with obstinate courage, and the enemy were eventually compelled to retire."

(Pandarus, while listening attentively, is covertly watching Cressida and Antigone. We may presume that he himself has had private knowledge of the facts beforehand, as he shows no surprise).

"In a daring attempt to rescue Captain Antenor, Lieutenant Troilus was slightly wounded, but we are reassured that the injury is in no way serious. This brilliant young officer's conduct in the field has been so exceptional that an official gazette has just been issued promoting him to the rank of Captain. Folks, I know you will all join with me in congratulating this well-deserved honor. Captain Troilus has been granted several days leave to recuperate, and plans to go out of town for a brief rest, as exclusively reported in tonight's *Evening Trojan*. Read your newspaper for full coverage in News, Editorials, Features, Advertisements.

"Just a word more, friends, before the sand runs out. To show how little our morale has been disturbed by hard going in the field, the social life of the season continues unusually colorful. Miss Lyde, our ubiquitous quidnunc in modes and manners and all Milady's interests, tells me that much smart entertaining is being done. The outstanding function of next week, of course, will be the dinner planned by Lord Pandarus in honor of his niece Miss Cressida. This might almost be described as a second coming-out party; Miss Cressida has not been mingling with the gay throng for quite some time; but her uncle very properly thinks that in times like these we need all our——well, shall I say, available social assets. Miss Cressida rates as one of the most charming, and while no list of the guests has been made public it is certain that some of our most prominent citizens are looking forward to Lord Pandarus' hospitality."

Dares brings in the tray of tea, and serves it during this palaver. Pandarus now waves to him to turn off the Voice, which the butler does as soon as he can; but not until the following has also been endured:——

"It's characteristic of our fair city that society refuses to let the campaign darken its spirits. Since more expensive entertainments are taboo, old fashioned parlor games have become all the rage this season and have afforded many a laugh in exalted circles. I've been told that the favorite of them all is that jolly old diversion of our youth, Sardines, or Hide in the Dark. I guess most of us remember that the technique of the game involves a good deal of intimate personal juxtaposition. Is my face red! I hear that when the current broke down at the power plant the other evening, a certain exclusive group on Pantheon Place never even knew about it. All the sardines were so much enjoying their game. Folks, it all goes to show that it takes more . . ."

As the radio stops, Uncle Pan is politely passing cakes, which Antigone accepts but Cressida declines.

Antigone cries impulsively: O, I do hope he's not badly hurt? He was so *wonderful* the other night.

Only a scratch, Pandarus says. I called up the barracks.

I was so ashamed, chatters Antigone, if I hadn't danced with that terrible man, we wouldn't have had that riot. I just didn't know what it was all about.

(Antigone, we very likely observe, is not always quite as naïve as she seems. She is covering up for Cressida, who is studying her own feelings).

I'm glad he's going away, Antigone continues. Poor fellow, I thought he looked tired.

I don't know anything as tiring as bending spears into hoops, says Uncle Pan; unless it's writing poetry.

O, stop it! Cressida bursts out angrily. Do you like to sit here and be humorous while brave men are risking their lives?

We might expect Uncle Pan to be taken aback, but he seems calm and merely performs the assiduous host. Cream or lemon?

I don't want any tea. I'll go and walk round the garden.

Have a look at my delphiniums, I've been raising them for the flower show. I'm going to name one of them after you.

You certainly have a genius for making things complicated, Cressida says as she leaves.

Antigone looks a little worried at this tantrum.

Let her walk it off, says Uncle Pan.

I'm sorry; she's a bit jittery. That mix-up at the dance was rather a shock to her.

Try to keep her cheerful. Everything's under control.

She hates so much publicity.

It has its purpose. Did you ever hear of camouflage?

Something to wear, isn't it?

You pretend to make a thing very conspicuous, but actually it fades out of sight.

Antigone doesn't quite understand, but enjoys her tea and prattles on. She's so marvellous, you know how I adore her. But she really has been upset about something. I can always tell, when she spends so much time at her music. It's her way of keeping me quiet.

Dares appears with very much of an air. He announces Captain Troilus.

How splendid! cries Pan, apparently surprised. How are you? all right? Come and sit down, take it easy. You know Miss Antigone? Isn't it nice to introduce you as Captain. My dear fellow, congratulations! I'm so glad it's the left, we can still write verse, what?

And with plenty more fluency he gets the embarrassed Troilus into a chair. The boy, in civilian clothes, has his left arm in a sling.

Glad you're out of uniform for a change. No tea, you need something stronger. Brandy for heroes, you remember. Dares, brandy and soda for the Captain; not too much soda. This is grand, how very good of you to come. Antigone, take care of Captain Troilus while I tell our other guest.

He bustles off, leaving them rather flustered. Both start to say something at precisely the same instant; politely abandon it, and beg each other's pardon.

I'm so sorry, he says.

I was only going to say, is it all right for you to be out?

O sure, this isn't anything.

I guess the Greeks are all just laying for you, after what happened the other night. We thought you were marvellous. I don't know how you did it. You must be frightfully strong.

It wasn't really strength. Just a kind of trick. There's a knack in it.

And that nice Captain Antenor who was having such a good time; what a shame!

Yes, bloody bad luck.

There's a pause. Troilus, out of topics, looks desperately at his left hand as a conversational memorandum, but is dismayed to find it swathed in bandages. This movement Antigone naturally misinterprets.

It *does* hurt, I can see.

No, it's only a scratch. Really. I say, what pretty clothes you—and your friend—were wearing at that shindy.

Did you think so? I'm glad. Cressida's afraid they were what made all the trouble.

I guess there'd have been trouble anyhow. It was about due.

(As his left hand is no use, he looks at the right, but that is occupied with the brandy and soda; so he takes a drink in hope of inspiration.)

I guess a war's rather a nuisance for people who aren't actually taking part, he ventures. How do you get along for amusements? Have you been reading anything worth while?

It's the funniest thing, I don't seem to get any chance to read. I don't know where the time goes to. There's always something. Cressida's cleverer than I am, she always finds time for her harp. She composes the loveliest little tunes sometimes. She writes them and I try to sing them for her.

The harp's a wonderful instrument, he says,

groping for more material. Except in damp weather, it's so hard on the strings.

Isn't it awful? I woke up in the middle of a wet night and thought I heard a bullfrog in the tank. It was the A-string in the fifth octave, going boom.

Troilus is still using his fingers as mnemonics. Speaking of bullfrogs, I don't suppose you're interested in politics?

This is so unexpected a leap that Antigone can scarcely follow, but at this moment Uncle Pan and Cressida return from the garden. He makes the unnecessary introduction. Well, this is delightful! I've been wanting you two to know each other . . . and gives Antigone a peremptory hint. Come and see the flowers, I want to show you something special.

Now the subtle balances of hesitation are past. Cressida knows it, feels the downward slope as she crosses the room. No need, or no use, to say longer what she has been reminding herself for days: "I don't have to love him if I don't want to. I don't have to love anybody." He looks so frightened, poor boy. Pain, fatigue, shyness, disbelief, all have shaken him; and he has used for Antigone all he can remember of his prepared syllabus.

They stand alone. Her eyes take pity on his trouble, and she has forgotten her own. Something clearer than sight, lighter than thought, passes from her through to the quality of his being, and is received where mannerly evasions no longer exist. She meets, and confers, something strong, simple, hungry, and intact. Something in man she never guessed before; never had chance to guess. Something in woman she had not known how to give.

He is first to falter; he sits, not quite knowing what he does.

I'm sorry. He starts to rise again. Gently she checks him.

Stay where you are. (She sits beside him). Don't say you're sorry. You've been saying it too often.

This is a thought so new, he requires a moment to consider it.

I meant, I've used up all my politeness on your friend. I've got nothing left, except things people don't say.

We say different kinds of things; don't we?— And then, her voice breaking into an almost angry tenderness: I didn't *want* to meet you.

He looks at her, worshipping. I didn't want to meet *you*.

I said I *wouldn't* meet you, she whispers; but you need me so.

Can I just sit and look at your eyebrows? I wanted to stand on them and look over the edge.— I guess that needs explanation.

The blue of the delphiniums is draining out into the dusk when the others come in. She is sitting on cushions at his feet, and they are talking quite calmly. They don't even bother to rise, and no one seems startled.

I suppose the tea's quite cold, says Uncle Pan. Well, we can all have a brandy and soda.

Darling, cries Antigone, that delphinium he's chosen for you is the loveliest thing I ever *saw!*

Did you find anything to talk about? asks Pandarus, using the emptying syphon to make a squawk of derisive exhaust.

Cressida looks at him over the rim of her glass. If I were naming a flower for *you*, I'd pick belladonna, or deadly nightshade. Something poisonous!

XII

PULL UP THE PUFF.

It is the close of Uncle Pan's dinner party. The guests, by Trojan custom, sit at one side of a long table; except the two of highest honor, King Priam and Queen Hecuba, who have their places at the ends. Queen Hecuba, at the foot of the board, has Pandarus round the corner on her right. From Pandarus upward they sit in order thus: Helen, Aeneas, Antigone, Deiphobus, Andromache, Paris, Creusa, Hector, and Cressida. And so Cressida is next to King Priam, on his left.

Evidently the host has been making a speech of courtesy, and in formal meter as demanded by ceremony. There is polite clapping by the guests. Dares, the butler, has been passing along the line filling glasses. Pandarus concludes:—

. . . But soft, I grow verbose. In goblets flush
I crave your kind attention. Here is health

To crown and doublecrown our little feast:
So, friends, the King and Queen!

(More polite applause)

PRIAM: My lord, and fellow guests, the
   Queen and I
Are copious of your gracious plenitude
And fed with wit as well as provender.
Now let us doff the formal; let our talk
Be casual, and in unconsidered prose. . . . It was
delightful of you to have us all here, and especially
for so pleasant a purpose. My dear (to Cressida)
you're not going to shut yourself up any longer. We
want to see something of you.

(As the talk becomes general, we can't help
overhearing scraps of conversation along the table).

HECTOR (to Creusa): There wouldn't have
been any war if we'd had a proper army. The only
way to avoid war is to be prepared for it.

ANDROMACHE (to Paris): Helen looks so
perfectly lovely. How does she manage to keep her
skin so dazzling. . . . (She checks herself from saying "after all these years"). . . . She has the most
beautiful neck.

PARIS: She takes after her father. You must
remember, he was The Swan.

DEIPHOBUS (to Antigone): Epsilon, Two-one-one-two. I never forget a number. What are you doing Saturday?

AENEAS (to Helen) : If I ever get a chance, it's certainly going to be one of those Mediterranean cruises.

PANDARUS (to Hecuba) : I wouldn't be surprised, that property out towards Ida's going to be valuable. I could cut the King in on some lots at a bottom figure.

HECUBA: I wish you would. It's so hard, with such a big family, to make ends meet. I kept warning Priam we ought not to have so many, but he's terribly persevering. Of course, as a bachelor, you wouldn't understand.

PANDARUS (to Helen) : Who started the legend that bachelors never understand? (to the table at large) I've got a little surprise for you all. I asked Princess Cassandra to come to dinner, but she pointed out that would mean thirteen at table—

PRIAM: I shouldn't think a little more bad luck would bother her. She's prophesied all there is already.

HELEN: It makes me feel rather uncomfortable. She always implies that it's all my fault. I can't help it if I'm—I mean, if I was made the way I am.

HECUBA: Poor Cassie: she's always been our problem child. It was such a mistake for her to major in, what does she call it, eschatology. I always say, there's enough trouble in the world as it is without looking into the future. Besides, all that business with entrails and sacrifices, it doesn't seem quite nice.

PRIAM: You're right. When I was young I went on a campaign against the Amazons and that cured me of professional women. Woman's place is in the home.

HELEN: Yes, but in *whose* home?

PANDARUS (hastening to avert an awkward topic) : I started to say, Cassandra promised to come in after dinner, with Troilus.

HECUBA (she has taken out her knitting) : That's nice. I didn't know the boy was back in town.

PANDARUS: He's coming specially for our party. He phoned me, his arm's all right again.

HECUBA: Well, I'm glad to know. I never see him any more since he left the palace. He took lodgings somewhere to be on his own. The younger generation is so independent. I don't suppose he gets his clothes mended, or regular meals, or proper sleep; and he was always delicate.

HECTOR: He doesn't look delicate out on the field, mother; you ought to see him.

HECUBA: Of all the children, those two are the hardest to understand. Priam, I don't know what we can have been thinking of. Maybe they got mixed somehow, born together like that. Here's Cassandra, uses such terrible language, really I don't believe the broadcasting station understands it or they'd cut her off; and Troilus was always such a gentle little thing. Do you remember, Father, how he used to play with dolls?

DEIPHOBUS: He don't seem to care for 'em grown up.

HECUBA: I tried so hard to give them all the right training and eat their cereal; of course I know this affliction of Cassie's is embarrassing, that mind-reading habit; she knows exactly what everyone thinks and naturally it upsets her; and now here's Troilus gotten so unsocial and conscientious, I don't think it's good for a young man to be so thoughtful and it don't seem natural in this family. All the rest of you were so normal, he really ought to—

PRIAM: Excuse me, Mother, I think Pandarus was trying to say something.

PANDARUS: No hurry, no hurry. Well, if you insist, I was thinking you might enjoy a little music. I asked Cressida to bring her harp, and Antigone is going to sing for us.

HECUBA: That's very kind of you, my dears, it really is. Cressida, your uncle tells me you compose.

CRESSIDA: Only a little, your Majesty; for my own pleasure, when I find something I like very much.

ANTIGONE: She's done this lovely setting for a new song, Lord Pandarus wrote it himself.

HECUBA: You mustn't be offended if I drowse; music after meals always puts me to sleep.

(Dares brings the harp forward; they are about to begin when Cassandra and Troilus enter. There are no special symptoms of "eschatology" about Cassandra except shell spectacles).

PANDARUS: Oh, good; here they are, just in time.

CASSANDRA: Surely. We wanted to get here before the storm.

PRIAM: Storm? This bright evening? Nonsense, child.

(Cassandra shrugs with a take-it-or-leave-it air. She is accustomed to disbelief. She and Troilus dutifully salute their parents).

HECUBA: You make me think of my old mother. She was always saying to us children, "Pull up the puff, a storm's coming." A puff was what country folks used to call a quilt or counterpane.

CASSANDRA: Pull it up then, darling; all the way to your chin.

PANDARUS: You know everybody, of course; except my niece, Cressida, and her friend Antigone. My dear, this is Princess Cassandra; and Captain Troilus.

HECUBA: Glad to see you, boy. Sit down by your old matriarch. Everything all right?

TROILUS: Just fine, Mother.

HECUBA: You still have your arm in a scarf.

TROILUS: That's mostly swank. It's practically well.

Pandarus signals to Antigone to go ahead. Please don't be too critical, she says to the company: I've never sung this before. Cressida wrote the music just the other day; Uncle Pan gave us the words:—

If, in days of sullen air,
    Dark with anger, dull with grief,
Merciful and unaware
    There transpire, for thy relief,
        Lighter mood or cleaner sky—
        Look no further; it is I.

Bandaged close and held apart
    Are thy mortal wounds that bleed,
Yet some subtle healer's art
    Touches on thy secret need:
        What physician, then, to bless?
        I it was, eased thy distress.

Beauty never guessed before
    Now is casual to the gaze:
Laughter copious to restore

All the waste of barren days:
    Cistern water turned to wine—
    Yea, these miracles are mine.

Under Zeus' immortal nod
    I am passion undefiled:
I, the child that is a god
    And the god that is a child.
        Canst thou not identify
        Thy magician? It is I.

Troilus, who has scarcely listened to what was said, is taken unprepared. At first it is the joy of looking: she cannot disturb him by returning it. The skill of fingers taking melody from the tall harp is one of earth's prettiest sights: such seeming mixture of chance and choice: deliberated and sure, yet also a sweet deception of apparent luck, of easy concord unprepared. Ripple, tremble and float: it releases tones as softly as a tree sheds autumn leaves. And O beauty of the hand that plucks and pauses; curls, beckons, then clasps and welcomes the shy music, child invisible, embraced between strong arms. Invitation surely, such teasing flickering gesture, summons and sweetness on the imagined breast. Then the full-grown strings, farthest away, reached for and struck, deep-rumbling or plangent, drill strangely on the twinges of delight. Added to curious looking comes the listener's lust: a fresh clear little voice, Antigone's, and a tingling naiveté of timbre; as though the dainty cadence were mere sound without meaning. But meaning keeps chasing slippery sight and sound; and he is astonished to find: the meaning is his own. These are his private words, whisper of past vigil, anger or folly in a forgiving dark; now they return, confident with music and bringing her with them. Meagre little verses that pretended bravado: now they sound strong: and riding on the very grace and instinct of her hands: the words become hers as much as his. All this he feels between chord and chord; it has no speech; no outward sign.

There's a babble of pleasure. Really, that was enchanting. . . . Why Pan, I had no idea. . . . You ought to publish it. . . . A very sweet voice, dear . . . a delightful treat. . . . We ought to have a benefit recital for the Red Cross. . . . Wouldn't you do an encore. . . . What do you call it?

A Song for Eros, says Cressida. I'm afraid I'm terribly out of practice.

Troilus seems to be analyzing the stitch of the knitting in his mother's broad lap.

Well Ma, says Priam, I think we better get along. (Troilus rouses her gently from her deep-heaving snooze. Pull up the puff, Mother, he murmurs.) Priam thinks they better leave the young folks to their parlor games, he has some papers to go over.

Hecuba revives without a struggle. Did I snore? Yes Pa, and I've got to get out some camphor balls tonight, I found a moth in your underwear.

Why bother, says Cassandra. The whole town will be in mothballs soon enough.

Pandarus, anxious to avoid any unpleasantness, intervenes quickly. I'm sorry you're going; we thought it would be fun to play charades, or a scavenger hunt, or adverbs; something we can all join in.

Cassandra, dreamily, as though not quite aware of what she is saying :—

Yea, parlor sports, charades and scavengers!
In the world's ruins, scavenging indeed.
What price charades against a coming storm?
The gods throw loaded dice, and play to win;
Troy falls, and with it aristocracy,
And civilization, that best parlor game,
Dumb cramboes to its end. . . .

PRIAM: Cassandra! Please! No vaticination!

HECTOR: Take it from her, Troy's going to make a regular habit of falling.

HECUBA: Really, I don't know what gets into the children. Cassie, come out of it! If you feel one of your spells coming on, try to control it. Not at a social party, please.—We've had a lovely time, Lord Pandarus.

Cassandra comes out of it; and now the old people have left there's a fresh round of drinks and argument what will most amuse. It's no use to play guessing games with Cassie, Aeneas says; she knows all the answers beforehand.—We could play Sardines, says Deiphobus (with his eye on Antigone) if we make Cassie *It*.—That's true, says Helen (who also likes the game) it won't matter even if she goes clairvoyant, because *we'll* be hunting for *her*.—So the rules are expounded: all lights out; Cassie allowed two minutes to hide; all the others to try to find her in the dark. . . .

They look speculatively round the extensive chambers, privately noting likely places where they think she may conceal. The patio with its pool and pillars, the balcony above, the big oak chests and wardrobes.

No fair going in the garden.

Please be careful groping round, Pandarus appeals; don't break the furniture.

Especially Uncle Pan's monocle, says Cressida.

Don't fall into the fountain.

Don't bash Captain Troilus's arm.

Needn't worry, he says; it's perfectly all right. I'll take it out of the sling so it won't be in the way.

All except Cassandra are leaving the room, to

give her a chance to hide. In this general movement Cassandra draws Troilus to her. She whispers: Shall I tell you where to find her in the dark?

His face is sufficient answer.

You'll never make a good liar, she teases.

Why not? (He thinks he has done pretty well).

If you never met her before, how is it you're wearing her scarf?

XIII

"*A WEDER FOR TO SLEPEN*"*

V<small>ELVET DARKNESS, WARM AND</small> thick. Behind the courtyard a slow punctuation of fireflies in the garden. Sparks, perhaps, to set off tightened pressures in the air.

Beyond the farthest pillar, as Cassandra foretold:——

Is it you?

Look out, your poor arm.

Cressida?

I won't tell you.

If I could see your eyebrows I'd know.

"Canst thou not identify?"

My sweet. O my sweet, your music.

Uncle Pan writes well, doesn't he.

They *are* your eyebrows. I memorized them. I believe there are silkworms in them. There are! They crunch like bacon.

* *Troilus and Criseyde*, III, 657.

Don't be so carnal.

That's not biting; only nibbling.

It isn't fair to memorize things without permission.

How about my poem?

I didn't memorize it. It just came in and sang to me.

It's yours now.

It's ours.

Poems need to have someone to sing to. That's been my trouble.

I was so afraid they'd make me play before you got here.

They don't know. How could they?

That's what I kept saying to myself, they don't know about Us.

I don't know very much myself.

We can find out.

I didn't dare come to dinner. I used my arm as excuse.

Blessing, you're clever.

I can't stand that sort of thing. It frightens me, my mind can't catch up, I have to say things I don't mean.

But that's the way *I* feel too!

I've never been able to talk to people. I've got years of it packed up inside me.

All right, we'll unpack it.

Can I put my arm—

Careful; is it the good one?

They're both good. Look. I mean, feel.

Help! I'm not one of those Greek spears you twist in circles.

Let's forget Greek spears for a moment. I'm going back to duty in the morning.

This is Now. We can sit down somewhere. There's a big chest over this way, I cracked my shin on it . . . come, this way. Shhh. Step gently.

Do you suppose we ought to go on hunting for Cassie?

(They listen. There are a few small sounds in the darkness: a stumble, followed by a muffled ouch, a whisper, a laugh quickly shushed. Someone says: I bet she's behind this curtain. Another voice: No she isn't, *we* are.)

Everybody seems happy, Cressida murmurs.

Do you realize, he says, this is the first time we've seen each other by ourselves.

If you call it seeing.

"So holds my love upon your rocky heart."

That isn't my heart.

It isn't rocky, either.

I liked that line about crank support.

This is it. Comfortable?

Mmmmm. Where do you get such attractive words?

They were all I had. I didn't have anything else. They're lonely sort of company.

They were just what I needed.

I thought I was the one who needed things.

If you really need anything, it must exist somewhere. I mean, the one implies the other; there must be some satisfaction or you couldn't feel the need of it. I don't explain very well.

You explain everything.

There couldn't be my kind of a Me unless there was your kind of a You, that wanted it.

My sweet. Or *my* kind of a You and *your* kind of a Me.

Now I'm confused.

Isn't it adorable that we both didn't want to meet each other.

Is that good grammar? I get so mixed up about pronouns.

We'll stick to nouns: persons, places, and things.

When did you first have an idea about Us?

I knew, as soon as I saw you at the temple.

I knew when you rode by the house. I was sorry for you.

Sorry?

You looked so full of—destiny.

That sounds like poor Cassandra.

Yes, and we'd better skirmish round and pretend to hunt for her.

Tell me some more, about when I went by your house.

I was only trying to keep things simple. I was making up my mind to grow old gracefully.

Don't make me laugh.

It hurts to get fond of people. I know. Don't get too fond of me, my sweet.

(There is a pause; then her voice continues) :—

That was the day you sent me to the dictionary. I made a poem about it myself.

Tell me.

It's not very beautiful.

Tell me anyway.

Well, let me get my breath. "Since he believes in dichotomy, I'd like him to think quite a lot o' me."

It came true, so it must be a good poem.

Troilus, isn't it fun to have someone to have fun with.

You'll have to help me, because I don't think I have much sense of humor. . . .

Imperative sound, sharp and urgent, edged with metal, tears the soft black hush. A telephone bell, ringing, ringing. Shrill with purpose, insistent, frightening.

Startled silence; then titters, whispers, furtive stir. But no one moves to answer the call.

Maybe something important, says a voice.

Shucks, it's up to Pan, it's his phone.

He seems to be occupied.

The bell keeps ringing; its persistence makes us a little uneasy. Then the voice of Dares :—

Hello? . . . No, this is the butler speaking. . . . I'm sorry, Lord Pandarus is engaged at the moment. Will you give me the message? . . . Hello, hello; are you there?

(He rattles the receiver).

I beg pardon, miss, I'm disconnected. . . . What did you say, Long Distance? O, a trunk call? Very good, get onto it. . . . 'Ung up? . . . Pardon me, I came with the utmost celerity. . . . Right you are; thank you.

There is the click of the instrument replaced. But almost immediately the bell rings again. We hear Dares mutter Blast! and reopen the circuit.

Well? . . . Why not say so before, it's a blinking nuisance. . . . To call operator fourteen and reverse charges. . . . What station, please? . . . Very good, thank you . . . 'kyou.

Some bloody Greek, Dares grumbles. Calling up this time of night. We don't pay any attention to unidentified calls. Blimey, it's a social stumor.

Laughter and comment from the various guests :—

Pan doing business with the Greeks on the side?

Maybe they want to quit and go home.

Helen, Menelaus wants to know if you're in bed yet.

It's not Menelaus, he'd never reverse the charges.

Say, is that thunder?

Cassie was right about the storm.

Cassandra's voice is heard, clear and cool: Are Pan and I the only ones playing this game? We've been sitting here I don't know how long.

Not too long for me, my dear, says Pandarus. —Dares, give us some light.—The butler does so, abashed to be revealed in his dressing gown, and hastily retires. Pan is discovered (refixing his monocle) seated comfortably with Cassandra on the stairs that rise to the balcony. Behind pillars and from recondite lurkings the others emerge in twos: Hector with Helen; Paris with Creusa; Troilus with Cressida; Aeneas with Andromache.

It's a difficult game, says Uncle Pan mischievously. None of the husbands seem to be able to identify their wives.

Deiphobus and Antigone are the last to appear. I'm sorry, she says, I lost my fillet in the dark.

I hope that's all you lost, says Paris.

I didn't know sardines came in pairs, remarks Cassandra. Usually they're packed in larger consignments.

So many places to look, it takes time.

I recognized Helen by that Shalimar she uses.

We were just hunting in that corner when the telephone rang.

It's rather startling when it goes off suddenly like that.

Listen to the wind! Cassie, you ought to work in the weather bureau.

And rain! I bet I left my bedroom window open.

It was ordained, says Cassandra serenely.

Cassie, that's a complex, Hector retorts. The only things ordained are parsons.

I'm glad for you to think so.

It's a pity to break up the party, says Creusa, but I'm afraid Aeneas and I will have to scoot. If the children have kicked off the covers they'll catch cold.

Yes, we better hurry before it gets worse.

I can give someone a lift, Deiphobus suggests. Antigone?

That's fine, says Pandarus. Go easy; don't skid.

We'll have a slippery field tomorrow, observes Hector. Get your sleep, boys; we've got some special stunts figured out.

Cassie, you won't get wet?

I told Troilus to order a cab.

Come on then, omniscient, says Troilus good humoredly. I'll see you safe.—Cassandra looks at him with affectionate indulgence; as if thinking, I wish I could say the same for you.—The vivid lightning and gathering rain make them all anxious to get away.

Cheer-oh, Pan; we've had a marvellous time. Thanks a lot.

Seeming to deplore their leaving, he is really managing the exodus. Can we give Cressida a lift, asks Andromache. You go along, Uncle Pan urges; she'll have to wait a bit, she can't take the harp in a rain like that.

Who's the harp? asks irrepressible Deiphobus.

Hadn't I better go with Antigone, says Cressida uncertainly.

Not a chance, cries Deiphobus, hurrying the girl away.

Psssh, my dear, murmurs Uncle Pan privately. Just bustle around a little, till they get off. You can't go out in this. Regular cloudburst. I had the guest room made ready for you, just in case. As Cassandra says, it's ordained.—Well, goodnight everybody! Come again soon!—Where *is* Cassandra? O, getting her cloak.—Troilus, my boy, here a moment. In your ear . . . come back here after you've taken Cassie home. We'll have a nice quiet nightcap together. Do you good.

You must want to turn in, don't you? says guileless Troilus.

I never go to bed. Why should I? No incentive.

Pandarus gives him a long look, and also the latchkey. Troilus seems puzzled, then alarmed, and is about to stammer something. But Cassandra returns, and bears him away.

Uncle Pan, sheltered in the big doorway, watches the cars slosh off in the storm. He closes the door against the wind, and rejoins Cressida; polishing moisture off his eyeglass; not a sentimental tear but blown drops of rain.

Something about the swish of that gale makes me think of a syphon. We might have a small stirrup cup. . . . Well, my dear, Zeus bless us all. A grand night for sleeping.

The thunder booms.

XIV

NEVER GUESSED BEFORE

In the earliest color of morning, Troilus at the window :——

If I could take a day that's beautiful,
Extend each lucid hour so wide and thin
Holding it up to let the light shine through,
I'd see the very tissue of elapse
Through which all being drains, the sub-
    stance leaks,
And glory sifts away.
I needn't have been frightened. . . . O secure,
Ascertained, accomplished, and made whole!
What heavenly simple strangeness :
The lady, proud and coveted from far,
So artificed and formally embellished,
Is found to be a murmuring human girl
Of legs and arms and slopes (such pretty
    handfuls

All silken in my hold.)
Is this, our natural and supremest worth,
What men befoul and leer with bawdy
    laughter
And snickers fouler still?

I guess why lovers call each other honey,
Which I thought vulgar use. The word is
    just:
The syrup sweet hath yet an edge of sour,
An aftersharp of acid, when we know
That oneness and the reaching deep delight
Imbued, and mixed, and pulsed, and perme-
    ated,
Is still so brief.
                    So brief.

                    Which would I rather:
She never wake, that I can study her
Without reproach of manners; or to rouse
And help me clog the sand, and slow the
    hour?
She's taken cover in a curly nest,
All nape and shoulder, haunch and bevel
    knee,
And what was wit and fury and surrender
Turns to the pathos of a sleepy child. . . .

CRESSIDA: Hullo!

TROILUS: Curled like the Argive spear
    you jested of,
You sleep with dormouse blood. . . . Nay,
    don't cover;
There's no need to conceal. It's only me.

CRESSIDA: I forgot where we were. Where
are we?

TROILUS: Together.

CRESSIDA: I'm not dreaming?—I think I *did*
have a dream.

TROILUS: It wasn't a dream. It was what the
grammarian calls a perfect participle.—I thought
that up while I was waiting for you to wake.

CRESSIDA: Blessèd idiot, I can't do grammar
before sunrise.—Really, I did dream. . . . Something rather beastly; I can't remember: it still feels
uneasy in the back of my mind.

TROILUS: Dreams go by contraries.

CRESSIDA: My sweet.—I know what would
solve everything. Every family ought to have an
Uncle Pan.—Happy?

TROILUS: Yes, if you just let me enjoy looking at you.

CRESSIDA: Biology makes better sense?—Get
me a cigarette, then I won't be so shy. I always wake
about four o'clock and have a smoke. Sometimes I
think, too.

TROILUS: It's a good idea. We'll do it regularly. What shall we think about?

CRESSIDA: Not anything. Just be Us.

TROILUS: Beauty never guessed before—

CRESSIDA: Now all casual to the view. It was a good prophecy.

TROILUS: Not casual. That's not the right word.

CRESSIDA: No. I don't like it either. Appetitive, maybe.

TROILUS: I guess it's important to check up a poem by actual experience.

CRESSIDA: We'd better go over each one and see if it's accurate.

TROILUS: I can see right away, there's a lot of revisions I've got to make.

CRESSIDA: You told me a terrible fib. You said you had no sense of humor.

TROILUS: I've been calling you white, in my mind. You're not at all :—
White's a bleached, flat, pallid, meagre word.
I'd say the color of the moon at full,
Or cream a little tarnished.

CRESSIDA: Please, darling : not before breakfast.

TROILUS: Perhaps there *is* no word. I'll
only say

The naked color of my Cressida.
Help me to be observant and exact
And never choose the word until it's right.

CRESSIDA: You can make a tentative statement, subject to improvement later.

TROILUS: Explorers always christen what
        they find,
Entitle it with meaning for themselves;
So, as discoverer in this pleasant land
I'll give to every place our private name.

CRESSIDA: You're divinely absurd. I like it.
It's nice to be—what would you call it?—proof-
read?

TROILUS: Secluded corners and smooth
        gradual slopes!
From tiptoe upward or from topmost down:
This nape you'll never spy, but which I see
A dusk horizon where the hair turns gilt,
Down to the very lowest least of you
Each item's worthy, holding shares of
        grace—
CRESSIDA: And draws its humble divi-
        dend of joy.

TROILUS: O, sight that has been trained
   on this devotion
And marched and disciplined in such a field
Will always see more clear, and hold your
   beauty
Etched in crystal figure on the eye.
I kiss the sweet sweet breast,
Saying it twice because there's two of them
And equal sweet. No favoritism here!

(*A bugle, very far*)

I go, before there's awkward observation.
I'm called for early duty.
CRESSIDA: Utmost dear, you need no
   words from me.
You have them all already; and me too.
TROILUS: One only, you must keep as
   talisman:
Remember: beauty never guessed before.
CRESSIDA: I hold it close.
TROILUS: If all men felt as I, it were
   today
Tough sledding for the Greek.
CRESSIDA: I love you, and not least when
   you're all soldier.
TROILUS: My honeysweet. Forgive the
   common phrase:
I go while going's good.

CRESSIDA: It is the best of kindness, and
    most rare.
Go swiftly makes the going less of anguish
And speeds next coming too. Before you
    leave
Turn the sandglass lest I overstay.

(*He moves to do so*)

No, don't! Let's keep it just like that.
TROILUS: Well thought. We leave these
    happy grains of Time
Just as they slipped through fortune's crooked
    neck
And made a mound of joy. A baby dune.
CRESSIDA: Unstable as all sand. Put it
    aside
Where nothing trembles it. . . .
                    And O, my dear
Be careful, for our sake!

XV

OLD FOX

ABOUT TWO HOURS LATER, while Cressida is still in a perfection of nescience, Uncle Pan quietly enters the guest room with a tray. In a faintly exaggerated representation of the perfect servant he draws curtains, delicately whisks out of sight anything that looks disorderly, straightens a vivid negligée and a pair of fluffy mules. Noticing the sand-glass set aside on the mantel he methodically turns it over and starts it running, checking it with his watch. Then he clinks the tray gently at the bedside.

Half rousing, she looks at him silently.

Shall I pour the coffee miss? Lovely morning after the rain. I hope the storm didn't keep you awake, miss. Nothing like a good sleep to renew the faculties. . . . Or would you like me to run the bath before you take breakfast?

She sits up, he hands her the wrap for her shoulders. Still she says nothing, so he brings her a cigarette and lights it.

I thought I'd wait on you myself. Dares is so easily shocked.

I can't quite believe that.

Nor can I. As a matter of fact, I've sent him out for some new harpstrings. I knew the damp weather would get them.

She seems impassive. You old fox, she says presently.

But a helpful old fox. He brings up a chair and sits, putting in his monocle. Have some coffee?

Is the cream tarnished?

Well I hope not. (He looks at it, rather surprised). Do you like it that way?

It's lovely.—What time is it? O damn your soul, you've turned over the sand-glass.

Certainly. Household routine. I like to keep things moving.

We wanted to keep it as it was. . . . Now it's all running out.

It's good for the sand. The more you run it, the smoother it gets.

I thought maybe it could stand still; just a little while. . . . O, Uncle Pan, what have you done to us? Don't make fun of me; I love him so.

So do I. I love you both. I must show you the

note he left for me. A little incoherent, but unmistakably grateful. Not a bread and butter letter, he said, but ambrosia and nectar.

I didn't know anyone could be so dear.

There, there, my poor child; now, now, now, you're upset. That's awfully good coffee, don't cry into it.

I'm *not* upset. I'm glorious, I'm magnificent, I'm a woman, I'm born again and never guessed before, but I can't help, you don't know, he won't ever; I mean—harpstrings aren't the only things that get broken.—Take away this cigarette, I'll burn up your lovely bed.

She holds it out to him as she turns to bury her face in the pillow. Uncle Pan takes the cigarette and holds it pensively, keeping a wise silence. After a pause she regains control, sits up again and takes back the smoke.

I'm sorry. It's my dormouse blood, just wanting to burrow out of sight.—I had a dream. I couldn't remember it when Troilus was here; I wouldn't have told him anyway, he was so happy. Then I went to sleep again and it came back to me: a huge horrible face, part animal and part human and something like a grotesque theatre mask. The mouth was wide open but it didn't move, and out of it came broadcasting, a harsh metal voice. I couldn't understand a word but it was full of hatred, a sort of gloating triumph. It was so positive, it sounded as though it must be true.

You've been thinking too much about those gas masks we saw. You mustn't let things like that work on your mind.

It was something like a gas mask, but also it made me think of that silly thing the Greeks have been building. Uncle Pan, it *was:* it was a horse's face, but huge, enormous, and I could see our men going up to it, laughing. They looked so small beside it, and suddenly I knew it was dangerous, it was coming alive. I tried to scream, and woke up.

And it was me.

O, I suppose other people's dreams always seem silly.

It was a nightmare—rather appropriate, by the way. If it's only the wooden horse, I wouldn't worry. We were talking about it at the club. Everybody agrees it's a big advertisement of some sort; probably for whiskey. The Greeks are great merchandisers. They figure if they can't beat us in war at least they'll sell us some goods.

I don't care what the damn thing is as long as it doesn't hurt *him*.

Let's be more cheerful, says Pan, going over to a radio built into the wall. I thought you'd like to hear Ilium this morning.

I guess I may as well give up trying to enjoy this coffee.

They're broadcasting from the battlefield, we might hear something interesting.

The Radio Voice:—

. . . so you can hear it for yourselves. (A far-away din of shouts, weapons, mixed noises). We're on the wall, overlooking the whole field. Fighting begins earlier these days, since the enemy have shown so much activity. Our men came on with their usual cheer, and today they're trying some new tactics. Colonel Hector is far out in the right wing, he has taken his infantry under cover down toward the river to try a flank movement, while Captain Troilus and the cavalry start a diversion on the other side. Troilus is back from leave, his arm is okay, and certainly he's making a wonderful come-back from his recent slump. Folks, I wish you could see this as I do, it's really impressive. All the boys are in great shape. King Priam and the general staff are up here on the wall watching attentively and it's easy to see they're pleased. Deiphobus is another who looks to be in top form, he's just led a rush of storm-troops into the center, he's raring to avenge the capture of his sidekick Antenor. There's some mighty smart work going on, wait a minute till I get the hang of this: yes, I can see Troilus signal to Aeneas, Aeneas and his crowd make a quick charge.

—Boy, that had those Spartans guessing—and Troilus has cut far out. He's turning, he's coming in on an angle, he's got them by surprise. He's in the thick of it. Wow! another Greek down. There he goes, there he goes, watch him—it's Troilus, folks. Say, that boy is breathing fire today. He certainly picked up some fresh pep on his vacation: I wouldn't be surprised he took one of those *Evening Trojan* bungalows down at Saline Shore, you'd hardly guess how bracing that air is, don't miss the coupon in tonight's paper.—He's taking on three Greeks at once, he's quick as a flash. He's down—no, only off his horse, he's all right, he's fighting on foot—he *is* down—only stumbled, just on one knee; he's up again. Achilles has noticed what a swath the boys are cutting, he's coming to back up the Greek line —and can he *come!* Everybody knows enough to watch out for Achilles; careful Troilus old boy; easy now, watch it; O, swell! Whew! Achilles aimed a savage one. Folks that was some stroke, terrific, but Troilus turned it. He's shaken off the others, he's taking Achilles single-handed, he's trading him sword for sword. Now Deiphobus is with him, they've got the big fellow boxed, he's got to give ground. There's a whole rally around them, I can't see for dust. Say folks, that's fighting. Now I'm going to turn over the mike to our military observer who'll give you the technical angle, but I just want to remind you . . .

Cressida gestures. Turn it off, I can't stand it.

Pandarus is pleased by what he has heard; he puts in his monocle and is rather demure. Something seems to have put our friend back in form. It just shows, we can all do our bit, one way or another. . . . I must toddle down to the office and do mine.

But Cressida still has something worrying her.

Uncle Pan, what was that telephone call last night?

Pandarus had not expected this, and seems a shade embarrassed.

To be frank, I don't know precisely. I rang Long Distance this morning, but when I found out who it was from, I didn't pursue the matter.

Something confidential?

I suppose I ought to tell you. It was your father, trying to reach you from the Greek Headquarters.

XVI

FAMILY AFFAIRS

Sunday night supper at Priam's palace is always an event. The whole family is expected to attend; but by reason of their numbers, and for patriarchal discipline, certain arrangements are necessary. The room is rather like a college dining hall, with ancient beams overhead and stained glass windows high in the walls. One side of the room is filled by a sort of grandstand erection, divided in two by an aisle of steps rising in the middle. The purpose of this will be evident in a moment.

The table is set for Priam, Hecuba, Helen and Cassandra. The two last are the only children who sit down with the King and Queen: Helen as their distinguished trollop-in-law, and Cassandra because of her embarrassing privilege as one touched by the gods. These four are finishing their meal; the sandglass on the table has almost sifted through. Fuscus

) 148 (

is serving: we may assume that the maids are given Sunday evening off.

But whatever the table talk is, we can't hear it at first, for outside the big closed door at the foot of the hall is a stentorian racket: a mixed jabber of talk, shifting feet, clattering on the heavy oak panels. This noise stills for a moment, then rises in the familiar music of the old Trojan song, shouted by some fifty voices:—

> Sparta had a son, Sparta had a daughter,
> When Trojan men they saw
> Their eyes were filled with water;
> Bone and grit they saw,
> Science, pluck and muscle—
> All King Priam's men
> Were ready for a tussle. . . .

And rising to a gibberish yell at the close of the stanza. This followed by miscellaneous clamor, and one clear voice: Hey, when do we eat?

Fuscus, whose lively negro heart is stirred by the air, waves time to it behind the King's back, until Priam catches his eye. He then decorously fills the King's wine glass.

Yassuh, King, he apologizes. I likes it when they gets enthused. Shall I let 'em in? I reckon dey mighty omnivorous.

Have you had all you want, my dear? says Priam to Hecuba, who is polishing her plate with a crust.

Nosuh, not all she want, but all dey is, ventures Fuscus. Who ever think ole Priam House come down to bread an' beans. Miz' Queen, dey's some left on Miss Cassie's plate ef you still hanker? Dese is craving times, sure enough.

That'll do, Fuscus, says the King. You can let the boys in, but I don't want any disorder. No shoving.

Fuscus goes to the serving table at the end of the room, where there is a big kettle of beans, a platter of bread, a pile of plates and spoons. He rings a farmhouse dinner bell, which causes instant silence outside. Before unbarring the door he shouts through. King Basilisk say no rukus. You-all know de rules: legitimates first.

Fuscus watches carefully as the legitimate sons pass in, orderly and in file, led by Hector. The slave counts them off, or pretends to (twelve, the total of two dice, is as far as he can go) but he soon gets his numbers mixed. Wait a minute, wait a minute, he exclaims, no pushin' folks. Excuse to me, Marse Phobus, aint you belong in de second lot?—Miz' Hecuba, what about Marse Deiphobus, don't he rate among de naturals?

Pa, I wish you'd get that settled, says the Queen placidly. It comes up again and again.

My dear, how can I possibly remember? I asked Cassandra to consult the oracle for us, but I suppose she's been too busy with her pacifist meetings.

Not at all, father, I worked it out for you by numerology. I don't know who his father was, but there's no question he and Aeneas had the same mother. They both vibrate 9; they're the only lucky ones in the whole crowd.

He and Aeneas? ruminates Priam. But I'm not Aeneas's father . . . (he snaps his fingers in sudden recollection) Zeus! Mother, you remember that snappy little Phrygian? . . . Deiphobus! You're a bastard.

Okay, chief, says Deiphobus, saluting respectfully and standing back.

If we were counting we would observe that eighteen legitimate sons file in. They are well-mannered, and pass in line along the serving table while Fuscus dishes out the food. But the slave is bothered. Ain't somebody lackin? Where's Marse Trolius?

No one seems to know. The eighteen go up into the right hand side of the grandstand; which, as we noticed before, is of two sections. The dexter side has 19 places; the sinister, 31.

Fuscus opens the door again and admits the

other sons. In this second group there is some grumbling about the fare. Sweet Ceres! crabs Deiphobus. Beans again! To which Fuscus: Yes, an' you-all lucky to get dat. All de professors say it's economics workin' on us. Chance-chillun got no call to be so finicky. 'Pears to me you-all make mo' fuss dan de regulars.

Priam and Hecuba (she with her knitting) sit back comfortably to admire the gathering. I always enjoy Sunday supper, says the King. It makes me feel we've really achieved something.

I can't help wishing there weren't quite so many of them on this side, Hecuba says, indicating the section of illegitimates.

They *are* a bit miscellaneous, observes Helen, turning to look at them; and ignoring a few cautiously dulcet whistles and yoo-hoos from the bleachers.

I'm sorry about that, the King admits. Careless. Well, trial and error. Helen, if you and Paris weren't so modern you'd be raising a housefull yourselves.

With that example in front of us? No thanks.

It's a pity they can't all sit down at a table and be refined, laments Hecuba with maternal solicitude. Their manners get so rough, and they eat too fast. Especially when it's beans, they're sure to suffer for it later.

There's one missing, Priam notices. Who is it?

Hand me the chart. Helen passes him a seating plan and he studies it. It's Troilus.

Hecuba is thoughtful: I've been worried about him lately. He used to be such a home boy, always busy at his books, and now when I call up he's never in his room.

Gracious, he's young, Helen exclaims. You can't keep them under lock and key. Look the way Paris got around. It looks like the old man did too.

That's neither here nor there, says Priam. Naturally we try to keep them from the mistakes we made ourselves.

We made, murmurs Hecuba calmly; with that much needed punctuation mark which would combine question and exclamation.

The editorial we; the royal we, suggests Cassandra.

The old lady perseveres her topic as she does her knitting. Cassandra, you know him best. Where does he spend his time?

But Cassie is not going to give away her twin. Why Mother, he's most likely with Pandarus. You know how devoted they are. Pan has a wonderful library, and he's gotten Troilus started on first editions.

Well, says Priam genially, if there's anything wrong with him I wish it'd happen to the others too. He's been wonderful on the field lately; extraordinary. I never saw such an improvement. That fight-talk I gave the boys certainly had an effect.——I guess they're about ready. Fuscus, you can ring.

The black rings the bell; there is immediate silence in the grandstand. All the sons' eyes are on Priam. He lifts his glass, looks toward the dexter section, drinks, and bows to them.

In unison they shout: Health, Father and Mother!

He does the same toward the others, who shout ——even a little louder, in rivalry or humorous defiance——Health, Father!

Thank you, Priam says politely. Boys, I want to tell you that I'm very much pleased. We've made real improvement lately and I think we have a right to celebrate a little. You know our old Sunday evening tradition: all the family together, open meeting, and anybody can say anything that's on his mind. Suggestions, complaints, arguments, feel perfectly free.

One of the illegitimates rises, timidly holds up his hand.

One moment please, says Priam. I'll have to consult the chart. Let me see, Row C, seat 6.——Ah yes, Cleon! Sorry, my boy, I should have known that red hair. Give my regards to your mother when you see her. Well?

If you please, sir, some of the boys have been

wondering, could we sometimes have a change in the menu—

He is shouted down by an outburst of mixed applause and jeers, groans, catcalls. These are primitive youngsters, and their emotions are near the surface.

Order, please! shouts Priam. A perfectly legit —I mean, a perfectly proper question. I admit we're getting a bit bean-conscious, but the rationing problem has its difficulties. Through the patriotic interest of Lord Pandarus, we were able to get a carload of legumes at a special price. I think some of them were a trifle mature, but we had to work them off. I'll refer the matter to the commissary.

Hector rises, holds up his hand, is acknowledged.

If you please sir, this is something I've hesitated to mention, but it comes under the head of family business. When I say family, I include everybody here, even Fuscus.

(Ironical cheers from the bastard benches: Hurray! Is Zat So! Thanks old boy! Fusky, take a bow! Who was Fusky's father?)

Just as a point of order, says Priam placably, allusions involving paternity are unparliamentary. Please remember, there are ladies present.

With much respect, that's what I'm coming to, Hector continues. I must ask if it might not be possible to put some restraint on Cassandra's pacifist activities. No matter how absurd they may seem, they are doing real damage to our morale.

Hear, hear! cries one of the illegitimates. All that crap has got me screwy.

Hector has the floor, Priam states.

My half-brother's phraseology is inelegant, but its purport is accurate. The T.L.D. meetings were bad enough, and so was the scandal at the Palladium, but those chiefly affected civilians. Now the poison's getting into the troops. They're all doing palmistry, telling fortunes with cards and tea-leaves, consulting dream-books and horoscopes, crystal-gazing in their shaving mirrors, and the latest hooey is numerology. Zeusalmighty, sir, are you going to let soldiers begin to think? It's fatal! It's not part of standard equipment. Once you sell them the idea that maybe this town is in wrong with the gods, you ruin their fighting spirit. It's bad medicine, and I want it stopped.

Hector's outburst brings great applause.

Son (says Priam slowly and gravely), you bring up something that's troubled me a great deal. Your sister's affliction is one that the gods themselves impart. The wise men tell us that she is under divine influence, and when the gods do things like that, they do it to try our faith. She has the Family Privi-

lege, and I'll ask her to speak for herself, but I do
hope she'll not try to influence us too much.

Cassandra, addressing the grandstand as though
she were a lawyer pleading to the jury:—

Not speaking for myself, but for us all.
You think that this is just the House of Priam:
No, it's the whole great world in microcosm,
And all the world's a Family Affair.
As children, we were quick to blame our parents
For all that went amiss; as men and women
We like to blame and scapegoat on the gods,
Or economic law or social pressure,
The follies of ourselves.
                              There's no such thing
As gods, or doom, or fate, but in the mind.
What care the gods if Troy or Sparta fall?
They are already fallen; and all those
Who hope to live by greed and hoax and fear.
The gods care nought who falls, or when or
        how.
The gods live only in the moment's beauty:
When the cicada lifts the noon with shrilling,
When the pinewood savors fresh of rain,
When the lovers bless each other's difference;
Or even when, in revenue of mirth,
Men laugh as you did here.
Athene, wisdom-spirit with clear eyes,

Takes many different forms, but mostly silence:
The gods are known by what they do not say.

O human creatures, skilled to calculate,
O sensitive beyond all other vermin,
Agile as frogs, and engineers like ants,
You are not doomed unless you doom your-
    selves.
Destroy yourselves in glee! And, re the gods,
See if they care!

There is an uneasy shuffling and silence; during which Helen rises and holds up her hand.

If you please, she says, I know I'm only an in-law, but I claim privilege. I haven't the faintest idea what Cassandra's talking about; there was only one line that made any sense to me. And I'm all mixed up: *are* we doomed or aren't we? I'd just like to say this, everybody here has been awfully decent, I've had a perfectly swell time and a lot of beautiful memories. I'd like to reciprocate: if things are really so bad, I'm willing to pack up and go. I dare say Menelaus would take me back. Would that help?

Furious yells of No! from the bleachers; and a rhythmic cry from the dexter side: We want Helen! We want Helen!

My dear, says Cassandra, I know it's painful to admit, but you're only a fortuity.

I'm not at all, I'm only thirty three.

Order, please! from Priam.

Deiphobus rises and is recognized.

If you please, sir, we on this side of the house feel that we have been somewhat slighted this evening. We claim Family Privilege.

The point is well taken, says Priam. Privilege granted.

We want to give our cheer.

Priam is a little dubious. Hum. Don't you think it's better to reserve that for barracks?

Point of order, sir, says Deiphobus respectfully. Privilege was granted.

True. Well, try to go a bit gently on that—you know. Fortunately your mother—I mean the Queen —seems to be asleep.

Deiphobus leads his thirty-one in their sectional yell:—

Proud! Proud! Say it loud!
This is Priam's left hand crowd!
Said to be: Said to be:
(*Whispered*) B—A—S—T—A—R—D—
(*Whistled*) Wh-e-e-e-e-e!
Helen! Helen! Helen!

General enthusiasm, but also some groans from the other side of the grandstand.

Paris claims attention. Privilege! he calls. Legitimate Privilege! Priam waves for silence and acknowledges him.

Beg pardon sir, but you'll surely permit a reply from those who had, if I may say so, benefit of clergy.

Unparliamentary, unparliamentary! shout the Left.

Must be fair to both sides, Priam admits, but looks a little anxiously at Hecuba, who is waking.

Paris leads the Right in a cheer. Come on now, short yell for Sons :—

> Left; Right—Left; Right!
> Priam loose, Priam tight,
> Try 'em, Priam, day and night!
> We're not sinister,
> We had the minister;
> Ask the oracle,
> We're historical
> Sons! Sons! Sons!

I hope I didn't snore, says Hecuba innocently. Did somebody drop something?

We'll drop the subject, says Priam. Helen, I think your question is answered by acclamation. Well, if there's nothing more—

Troilus bursts in through the great door, excited and out of breath. He draws himself up and salutes.

You're late, my boy.

Sorry, sir; I was detained. Lucky I was, because on my way here I met a sentry running from the Gate. I was the only officer he could find and I had to go down and take the message.

Message? Go on, boy, what is it?

The Greeks have asked for a truce. (He hands Priam a scroll.)

An enormous cry of exultation. O Boy! yells Hector. Cassie, who's loony now?

I must telephone the Council, says Priam. Dismiss!

Family Supper breaks up in jubilee. They pour out of the banquet hall : the King and Queen to their private apartments; Helen eagerly talking to Paris; the sons of both factions fraternizing gaily, and off to celebrate in their favorite pubs. Only Cassandra is left at the table, lost in thought.

Fuscus catches Troilus in the throng. Stick around, Marse Trolius, I fetch you some supper.

XVII

NUMEROLOGY

Fuscus must have secret sources
of supply, for he sets before Troilus a liberal platter.

Marse Trolius, you come like angels in underwear. Good grub for good news!

Favoritism, says Cassandra. She takes a tidbit
from her brother's plate and nibbles it. You're getting all sorts of favoritism, aren't you.

Don't tease me; I'm so happy.

I'm glad.—She watches him with deep affec-
tion.—You deserve it.

I had a notion the Greeks were a bit demoral-
ized. They acted queer all day yesterday. They had
about half their men monkeying with that fool
horse. They've put caterpillar treads on it; I believe
it's a kind of tank.

I got it all figured out, says Fuscus. Dey gwine
make it a diner-wagon, dey won't have to go back
to camp fo' ice cream cones and hamburgers.

But think of their actually calling for time. Gee, it's too good to be true.

Exactly, says Cassandra.

What do you mean?

Never mind; go on with your supper. What does it matter what I mean? It's what Daddy calls my affliction.

Now Miss Cassie, don't you be a nigger in de ointment.

Cassandra takes pencil and paper from her little bag. Fuscus, she says, I don't suppose you know much arithmetic.

No ma'am, I'm kinda reticent wid cyphers. I always fixin' to get hold of it some day, but ole War come along, dere don' seem to be no time fo' study.

Maybe I can make you understand. You know that numbers and letters are magic, they're what raise man above the animals.

Yes ma'am, I heah dat in chapel. De po' beasts, dey jes' skirmish aroun' in nacheral depravity.

Now you see, you put letters and numbers side by side, like this; for every letter you have an equivalent number.

Equivalent. Yes, Miss Cassie, jes' so.

All right. Now suppose you want to know your luck. You take a name—take your own name, Fuscus. See, I'll write it down.

Dat my name, Miss Cassie? It look right han'-some. Dibbies on dat paper, it bring me luck.

Well, we'll see. You add up the numbers that symbolize the letters of your name, and see what total you get. Remember that all our counting is based on tens; what they call digits; just like your fingers and toes.

Dass what throws me off, Miss Cassie. I ain' got ten toes. Dat first winter campaign I got fros'bite.

Never mind. All you need to know is, some numbers are lucky and others aren't. Deus numero impare gaudet. That means, the gods love odd numbers.

Nobody never took no trouble wid me befo'. Miss Cassie, ef dere's anything I got smatterings of, it's education.

You know what an odd number is?

Yes, *ma'am*. Dat's when two's company and three's a nuisance. De party don' pair off right. Odd number look out de window an' pay de taxi.— Seben an' eleben, dat's odd numbers, ain't it?

Quite right. And very good numbers too.

Ally oop! Marse Trolius you watch dis, you do better in dat crap game down to de barracks.

Cassandra is adding up.

I was afraid of that. I'm sorry, Fuscus, you've got an 8.

What's de matter wid 8, Miss Cassie? Ada fum

Decatur! I seen some right good combinations on an 8.

It's all hooey, says Troilus. Don't pay any attention.

8's my number too, if that's any consolation to you. And it's Lady Helen's.

What's good enough fo' you, Miss Cassie, I'll string along.

8's impossible. It vibrates wrong every way.

O, for heaven's sake, grumbles Troilus impatiently. That's terrible tripe, Cassie. Lay off it.

Let me show you something. There's only one number worse than 8, and that's 6. It starts out like good fortune because it's two 3's, but what looks like success turns into tragedy. Take Troy. T-R-O-Y-, that's 2, 9, 6, 7. Eleven, seventeen, twenty-four, makes 6. Then take Sparta: 1, 7, 1, 9, 2, 1—that's 21, makes lucky 3.

Shucks, try it as Lacedaemon.

That won't work; I can't spell it.

There you are! The whole thing depends on knowing how to spell. It's the bunk.—Try Priam.

You've got to take it the way the name is generally used. *King* Priam. Gives an 8 again.

Try Marse Hector, begs Fuscus who is hovering anxiously over them.

Hector's worse still. He's got a 6, and Achilles the same. Their destinies are tied up together.

Instead of Sparta, try Greece.

Doesn't help. A lucky 7. Or Hellas, a lucky 3. My dear old boy, the priests at the temple have been over these figures until we know them backward. Agamemnon is 11—Electrical Eleven they call it, the most perfect number there is. Menelaus is 9, almost as good; and here's something interesting: Paris is 9 also. Doesn't that show they were due to have the same luck?—if you call it luck.

What about me, asks Troilus, interested in spite of himself.

You're 33; that makes the misleading 6 again. And if you're skeptical, I can tell you someone else who's 33 also.

I don't believe it.

Look at the figures. (She shows him).

Gosh, that's right. I don't care what they are as long as they're the same. How is it if you add 'em together.

Soandso *and* Soandso—you've got to add the numbers for *and*—that's 6 and 1 and 6—makes 13. How do you like it?

Dass bad, says Fuscus. Dass curtains. Dass where I quit learnin' my numbers, when I come to 13. Miss Cassie, throw away dat paper befo' it give someone epizootic.

Try her full name. Cressida Calchas.

I never thought of that. All right: C-A-L-C-H-A-S.

Maybe he spell it wid a K, suggests Fuscus, trying to be helpful.

3, 1, 3, 3, 8, 1, 1. Total 20, that's a two. Double-faced two. Her old man lived up to it, didn't he? Add 2 to 6, you get the fatal 8.

O to hell with it! I won't listen to such dirt. Ever since that damned oracle prophesied Troy would fall and all the women would be ravished by the Greeks you've been hoping it'd come true.

Troilus rushes away in a rage. Fuscus, much agitated, seizes the sheet of calculations and burns it in the flame of a torch.

Cassandra is struck by this:—

Even the slave, unwitting, proves the same :
Our fates, however reckoned, end in flame.

XVIII

OFF THE RECORD

The war council. Priam, Pandarus, Hector, Paris, and three unidentified Brass Hats. Also Ilium, the Radio Voice (in person), who takes notes. Pandarus and Ilium wear modern dress; all the others in classic panoply.

PRIAM: Gentlemen, I called this emergency meeting to discuss a very unusual proposal. I even ventured to ask our friend Mr Ilium to sit in, representing the interests of the Press.

PANDARUS: Ilium understands that everything said here is off the record until a specific release is given?

ILIUM: Sure, sure. Is it all right to smoke?

PRIAM: The enemy have asked an armistice for the mutual return of prisoners; but on one condition. This was confidentially imparted to me by their envoy; they offer it as a valuable concession.

They will return Captain Antenor to us if we will send Cressida in exchange.

(The others show astonishment).

PARIS: We knew the Greeks were short of women, but that seems pretty brazen.

HECTOR: We haven't been accustomed to use women for military trading.

BRASS HATS (in unison): Outrageous!

PANDARUS: Timeo Danaos et dona ferentes.

ILIUM: Just a minute, old man; I don't get your slang.

PANDARUS: It means, the Greeks are most dangerous when they pretend to be friendly.

ILIUM: That's what I thought. Some hidden dirt. Yeah.

PRIAM: I agree, it sounds disgraceful at first; but let's discuss. The Greek note, stripped of its customary obfuscation of diplomatic jargon and insincere courtesies, reduces to three points. First, and I must say with characteristic effrontery, they remark that we have long had here in Troy at least one more woman than we need—

PARIS: Well, damn their crust! If they couldn't keep her, it's just too bad.

PRIAM: They're quite flowery about it. The exact text says (he refers to a scroll) "And whereas the aforesaid golden apple, awarded as the prize of beauty, has now begotten the hard cider of discord, unpalatable to both parties, we therefore . . ."

PANDARUS: Your majesty, it's a trick. Legal phraseology always means trouble.

BRASS HATS (always in unison): Look out for legal phraseology!

PRIAM: Second, they base their extraordinary suggestion on humanitarian grounds. They submit that from a military point of view this exchange is greatly to their disadvantage, but they say that Cressida's father, Doctor Calchas, is seriously ill and needs his daughter.

HECTOR: I don't think we owe Doctor Calchas any particular consideration.

ILIUM: I should say not. He blew like a tire, left your Brain Trust flat on its—I'm sorry.

PRIAM: I don't hold anything against Calchas. I was rather relieved when he left. I'm too old-fashioned to understand all those economic diagrams. I'm only thinking of the young woman.

ILIUM: He certainly shipped a carload when he got that filly. He didn't find *her* under a pile of statistics.

PANDARUS: May I remind the last speaker that—hmmm—it takes two parents to ship a carload. Speaking as her mother's brother, I think I have a right to protest against this proposal. I do not believe her father can be genuinely ill, since he was attempting to reach me on the telephone the other evening.

PARIS: That's queer.

BRASS HATS: Devilish queer.

PANDARUS: It makes me the more certain this is some stratagem.

PRIAM: He might have been telephoning because he felt that he was *going* to be ill. But allow me to proceed, gentlemen. I am in sympathy with the obvious arguments against this offer; but let me add, the Greek note categorically assures us that the lady would be free to return at her own pleasure.

ILIUM: Your majesty, nerts.

PRIAM: Possibly, possibly. But we Trojans have always made war chivalrously. I should be sorry if it were said, we refused to allow a girl to visit her father when he needed her.

BRASS HATS: Trojans are always generous.

PANDARUS: Suppose she doesn't want to go.

HECTOR: Pardon me, the question of military necessity takes precedence. If the girl is free to come back when she pleases, that puts a different aspect on it.

PANDARUS: Surely, Colonel, you don't trust any such pledge?

HECTOR: It would be very helpful to have Antenor. He is one of our ablest officers and we miss him seriously. Would we have to surrender him when Cressida returns?

PRIAM: They say not.

HECTOR: Antenor's worth half a regiment

of hoplites. I don't mind telling you, we could use him right now.

PARIS: I think I agree with Lord Pandarus. The whole thing sounds fishy.

BRASS HATS: Military necessity, military necessity.

PRIAM: We need the truce. It would give us a chance to replenish food supply.

PANDARUS: It would be a mistake to decide so important a matter too hastily. Your majesty mentioned a third point?

PRIAM: Yes, I was forgetting. It seems rather trivial, they throw it in as a sort of postscript. The Greeks say that if the armistice is accepted, they assume we would have no objection to their moving that Horse of theirs closer to the city.

HECTOR: That damfool Horse, I don't care what they do with it.

ILIUM: It's an advertisement of some sort, they want us to get a good look at it.

BRASS HATS: Ha, ha, ha, that damfool Horse!

PANDARUS: I don't like to seem argumentative, but even the Horse might be made the subject of protest. If it's an advertisement, it may be the beginning of a movement to scatter that sort of thing all over the countryside. Very distressing in our lovely Trojan landscape. Can't you imagine commercial effigies in grotesque shapes, an eyesore to the traveller?

HECTOR: Absurd! We're wasting time.

PRIAM: Surely, my lord, you are too fanciful. Not even the Greeks would be so vulgar. They say it's a Y.M.C.A. hut for the amusement of their troops, and they want to move it out of the sun, where it won't be so hot.

PANDARUS: I'm willing to concede you the Horse, gentlemen, if you will give more careful thought to the other matter.

PRIAM: The Greek envoy is waiting for our answer. There are really only two questions. Take the lesser one first; the Horse. Do we agree that during the truce the enemy can shove it around as they please?

ALL: Agreed.

PRIAM: Carried nem. con. Now the more important decision. In the exchange of prisoners, shall we allow Miss Cressida to visit the Greek camp, with full privilege of return, in exchange for the unconditional release of Captain Antenor? Is there further discussion, or are you ready for the question?

PANDARUS: My friends, before this is hurried to a vote I must say a word. I freely admit the great value of Captain Antenor's services, but I am convinced this is some ruse on the part of the enemy. Is it not possible that Dr Calchas, already an admitted traitor to our cause, hopes to pry some of our secrets out of a confiding daughter? And consider the case of the girl herself, thrown into the license and disorder of a military encampment. Do not think I am moved only by being her near kinsman. Here she has a home, friends, protection, and at this moment a chance to resume social usefulness after some years of domestic shock. Is it our Trojan chivalry to use one of our own children as a political pawn?

PARIS: Hear, hear! Very well said, my lord.

PANDARUS: I don't suppose anyone here is familiar with Chryseis and Bryseis—

ILIUM: Sure, I am. A couple of tarts.

PRIAM: Order, gentlemen.

PANDARUS: Mr. Ilium takes the words from my mouth, though I had intended a softer phrase. But such is the fact; Chryseis and Bryseis were a pair of our innocent Trojan country girls, too confidingly entrusted to the Greek headquarters. Gentlemen, their demoralization was complete. I've been told that they are now professional habituées of Sarpedoni's dance hall,—practically on the menu.

ILIUM: Sort of hors d'oeuvres.

HECTOR: Surely, sir, you show unnecessary doubts of the lady's stability? In any case, she will have her own father as chaperon. What more can we ask?

PANDARUS: And finally, consider the publicity aspect. If it becomes known that we barter our females for campaign advantage, it would make the name of Troy shameful for ages to come.

ILIUM: I can't imagine ages to come worrying about this old burg. They'll have troubles of their own.

PRIAM: Admitted that international traffic in women has its drawbacks.

BRASS HATS: Question! Question!

HECTOR: I move you, sir, that we accept the enemy's proposal.

BRASS HATS: Second the motion!

PRIAM: You have heard. All in favor of the motion?

(Hector and the three Brass Hats rise).

It is carried, four to three.—It is painful to go against the judgment of one of our most respected members, but I must believe that his forebodings are excessive.

PANDARUS: At least you will give the girl time to prepare herself for this deplorable event.

PRIAM: Hector, bring in the Greek envoy, we will discuss the necessary arrangements.

ILIUM: 1185 B.C. marches on!

XIX

SULTRY PINK OR PRICKLY PEAR?

I<small>N THE PRIVATE OFFICE OF</small> P<small>AN-</small>
darus and Company we find Uncle Pan gloomily
watching the ticker and dictating to a handsome
stenographer.——The first reaction to the armistice
announcement (he is saying) was emotionally favor-
able, but we note a curious uneasiness under the
surface. Heavy industries held firm, but chemicals
and rubbers were temperamental. No, Miss Dictes,
cross out temperamental. Say, chemicals and rubbers were soft. The drachma is being subjected to
severe pressure. The rediscount rate has been re-
duced, frankly a bad sign; evidently prompted by
the desire to bolster government securities. Direct
obligations of the Trojan government have fallen as
much as seventeen thirtyseconds. At this morning's
opening several leading issues are off. Confidentially, a considerable shade of pessimism is indicated,
though not necessarily immediate liquidation. Sin-

) 176 (

cerely yours.——It would be more sincere (he remarks, releasing his monocle) to say simply, things
look lousy. However, the ethics of the Street must be
observed.

The telephone rings. It's your niece, Miss
Dictes informs him.

How are you, my dear? . . . Not at all, not at
all. . . . Of course I want to help. . . . A tragic decision, I quite understand. . . . I don't know what to
say, I'm really not competent. . . . Just a minute, I'll
get expert advice——Miss Dictes, my niece is going
to the Greek headquarters for a few days' visit, she
has only room in her bag for one evening costume.
She wants to know which to choose: a dress of sultry pink with a wine-red jacket; or one in prickly
pear velvet with a tinsel bodice. Prickly pear, that
sounds very uncomfortable!

That's just the name of the color, smiles Miss
Dictes. It's a kind of green, the latest thing. I've
seen it in the window at Pygmalion's.

We advise the prickly pear, (says Uncle Pan into
the phone) but with a shade of pessimism . . . will
you say that again? . . . It's as technical as the stock
market. He turns to Miss Dictes: She says the
prickly pear outlines the bosoms with cupcustard
paillettes. What on earth are paillettes? Sounds a
little too milkmaid, don't you think?

It depends a bit on the figure, suggests Miss Dictes, amused. Is she rather full?

Really, I don't remember—In the family one scarcely notices these things—Hullo? We think perhaps, under the circumstances—I suppose the Greeks are not quite abreast of the latest modes—probably the pink; what was it, sulphur pink? . . . sultry pink—Yes. . . . Quite. . . .

Just see what Amalgamated Spearheads are doing, he asides to Miss Dictes. That's rather urgent.

Certainly, he continues patiently into the phone. Yes, the tweed-and-jersey travelling suit. Very appropriate. . . . Terrible, my dear, terrible. . . . I did all I could, but I was helpless. I'm at my wits' end. . . . Keep up your spirits, everything will work out somehow. I'll see you later.

He rings off. Miss Dictes lays a memo in front of him.

Down, eh? Begun to slide. Change the close of that letter. Instead of "not necessarily liquidation" say "probable liquidation." Please get that off at once.—He goes again to look at the ticker.

As the secretary leaves, Troilus comes in wildly.

I'm sorry, he exclaims : I couldn't wait to be announced. Pan, can't you do something? Zeusalmighty, fooling around with ticker tape while things are like this?

I did all I could. You understand, I couldn't be entirely frank in the council meeting. As it is, I expect they all think I have some sinister motive of my own for wanting to keep her here.

How is she taking it? I tried to call her, but the wire was busy.

Why she's—well naturally she's very upset.

Poor darling. Pan, I worship her, she's the most marvellous creature that ever lived. Look at this, (he rages, showing a paper)—I've been assigned the job of escorting her to the Greek lines. Was there ever such irony?

Perhaps we're taking this too hard.

Easy for *you* to say. I can't live without her. She's the only person who ever made life seem really beautiful.

Why don't you go away with her? Just take her and disappear. The Byzantium Road is still open, you can have my car. Slip off tonight and vanish.

I couldn't. I wouldn't be happy. I've got to be faithful to Troy. She wouldn't be happy either. We couldn't love each other if we weren't proud of each other.

Now don't let's dogmatize about love. You'll find out presently, it's very elastic, it can take a lot of punishment.

O, please don't be sententious. I'm in absolute misery.

But listen, my boy: she's only going away for a few days, to visit her father.

Do you think they'll let her come back?

Of course.

Never. I don't believe it.——If we got married before she goes, she'd *have* to come back. Do you think I could appeal to my father?

Impossible. He'd be terribly shocked.

I suppose so. Why do we always think other people will be shocked but we're never shocked ourselves.

A very merciful paradox. That's the only thing that keeps society going at all.

To hell with society, groans poor Troilus in perplexity and despair.

You know perfectly well, says Pan, in your position, a liaison could be tolerated; but marriage, never.

Disgusting.

Quite so; but there it is.

Pandarus looks irritably at the mass of papers on his desk. He has the busy man's distaste of discussing sentimental matters, however acute, during office pressure. His trained and sensitized imagination divines all the telephone calls that are tingling repressed in the instrument beside him; diverted for the moment by the capable Miss Dictes. The chancellor of the exchequer about the new bond issue . . . the Fuel Administration anxious to discuss plans for next winter's coal supply. . . . Not even his devotion to these young people can extinguish his desire to dispatch these complicated and urgent affairs. He presses the buzzer on the desk.

There's another consideration, he says. You know I'm as fond of Cressida—as fond of both of you—as if you were my own children. Fonder probably. But allow me to say, she's not the only woman in the world. While she's away you might look around with this new-found awareness of yours and —well, get some perspective. You'll be astonished to find how many lovely creatures there are; and not inaccessible.

Troilus is appalled at this wanton doctrine. He is almost speechless.

Really, he says. Well Zeusalmighty. . . . Next you'll offer me a little notebook of telephone numbers like Deiphobus has.

Very comforting sometimes. But please don't use *like* as a conjunction. I think I can honestly say, that is the only thing that really shocks me.

Miss Dictes has misunderstood her employer's buzzer; she supposes he has signalled for his lunch, and comes in bearing a plate of crackers and a glass of milk.

Thank you, he says. Please call the Treasury

office and tell them I'll have those figures ready by two o'clock.

I suppose it's being busy makes you so cynical, says Troilus. This damned Treasury-tickertape-tycoon atmosphere. You sit up here in your swanky office and run the world. Little things like love and separation and suffering aren't quoted on tape, are they.

Sometimes they are, says Pan gravely. But he sees that the boy is deeply hurt, his quick sympathy hurries to the surface. Please forgive me, I didn't mean to seem heartless. I'm just as cut up about this as you are; but let's not sell out before the market breaks.

O Pan, why does life keep pushing us around: couldn't things just stay put for a while? Only a few hours ago, everything was so lovely—

And will be again, I dare say.—Pandarus looks at his watch.—All the cynical and sensual tycoons are now mumbling their luxurious lunches. Graham crackers and milk. Will you have some with me?

I'm due at barracks. I'm sorry I bothered you; I'll try to be sensible.

Fine. You can do better than that. Come to my house tonight after dinner. Some of her friends are coming in to pay their respects, a sort of *pour prendre conger*. We'll get rid of them early, and you two can have some time together.

You do know I love her, don't you!

As Troilus goes out, the telephone cannot retain any longer. It rings fiercely. We leave Pandarus at his desk, phone in one hand and glass of milk in the other.

XX

HALF WAY ACROSS THE DARK

Pandarus's house; the patio in evening light. Coffee and liqueurs have been served. The ladies invited to say goodbye to Cressida are now leaving at last, with the usual female reluctance and multiplied valediction. Pandarus is easing them toward the doorway, where Dares skillfully completes the process of extrusion. Troilus (in modern uniform) stands on the outskirts of the group; he looks unhappy.

HECUBA: Well, my dear, I really must go.

TROILUS: Now mother, you're repeating yourself.

HECUBA: I hope you'll find your father improved. Take your knitting with you, it's a great consolation if you have to sit up late with an invalid. Troilus, are you coming with me?

PANDARUS: I'm sorry, ma'am, I'm keeping him a while; we have some business.

HECUBA: I really hate to go, this is the only house in Troy where one still gets decent coffee.

PANDARUS: You're very kind, ma'am. (But he takes away her cup so she can't ask for more) .— I'm afraid it's too strong, it keeps people awake.

HECUBA: That's just what I need.

PANDARUS: The ruling classes should spend at least half their lives in sleep. (He moves her firmly toward the door) .

HELEN: When you see Menelaus, be sure to give him my messages. Tell him not to do too much. If they win he'll have to take me back; that'll give him a scare.

ANDROMACHE: I think it's wonderful of you to do this for us; it's real patriotism. I'm going to write an editorial about it for the Junior League.

HECUBA: The Greeks are very attractive socially; don't let them persuade you to stay too long.

CREUSA: I'm sure you're tired, so we won't keep you.

PANDARUS: I know my niece appreciates so many kind wishes. I mustn't let her stay, she still has some packing to do.

HELEN: Goodbye dear, I envy you having a chance to get out of town.

ANDROMACHE: Try to find out what they're wearing in Sparta this season.

LYDE (the Fashion Reporter) : I've got a nice

little story for the paper, but I do want to know what Miss Cressida's going to wear.

PANDARUS: A blouse of prickly pear with a couple of cup custards.

LYDE: Perhaps I better send the photographer—

ANTIGONE: He means the moulded bodice effect.

PANDARUS: Storied urn and animated bust —let Antigone tell you.

CRESSIDA: It was so sweet of you all, I don't know what to say. I'll be back before you know I'm gone.

And now they have got them all through the door. Antigone goes off with Lyde, giving her some technical details. Aren't women terrible, says Cressida. The lowing herd winds slowly o'er the lea, observes Pandarus, waving farewells. He turns and sees that Cressida is already in Troilus's arms.—I guess this is one of those evenings when I take Antigone to the movies, he says; and leaves.

I couldn't have stood much more of that, Troilus begins harshly.

Don't say anything, she whispers. For a little while. Let me find *me*. . . . And, after a silence: Now say it.

What.

You know. Our talisman.
Beauty never guessed before. . . .
(She shivers a little in his arms).

TROILUS: This is the dress you wore at Sarpedoni's.

CRESSIDA: You know them now by heart.

TROILUS: Like a tree of fruit in April
        gear
You cloud your firmness and your branchy
        limbs
In gauze and silver bloom. But underneath
Yourself is whiter still.

CRESSIDA: You said white wasn't a good
word.

TROILUS: Tonight we will not stay to
        choose our words.
There will be time in surplus, nights to
        come.
CRESSIDA: No . . . no!—Then came our
        summer wind
And stripped me of my petals, and pretence.
TROILUS: That night you danced with
        Paris; and I thought:
Even her body, under all that lustre,
Is scarcely dark.

CRESSIDA: My mind is dark enough.
How black the thought must be, inside the
    brain.
TROILUS: Yes, black indeed. I was awake
    last night:
You know that gap half way across the dark
Where stars fall in, sleep founders, and the
    mind,
A frightened swimmer, elbows for the shore.
Then common things, acceptable by day,
Turn haggard; life is filthy on the tongue;
Faces that you love are old and sorry. . . .
O fill my eyes with whiteness
To help me through the dark; and smooth
    my fingers
On luxuries of touch
To keep a memory for empty hands.

CRESSIDA: Here is one face that is not old—
nor sorry.

TROILUS: And if long looking push the
    dark away
Then ears grow keen to horror:
The furious insect-chorus of the fields
Goes mockery-whistling on. The grassy
    troops
Are mobilized in all their murder-kit

For some last senseless onset of despair.
So are we all. Cassandra's right. We're done.
See this? A pretty symbol! Voice and face
Your insect cavalier; the praying mantis
Or prophet-beetle!

(He blows his trench-whistle, and whips out his
gas mask and holds it to his face; which does indeed
make him resemble some monstrous insect. Cressida
gently puts it aside).

CRESSIDA: Let's sit down and have a smoke.
—Will you pour me a drink?

TROILUS: Does every other feel *my* pri-
   vate pang,
The little secret stabs of circumstance,
The comic molecules that make me, me?
CRESSIDA: Yes, all; and all are cunning
   to conceal.
Of every midnight twinge that cramps the
   heart,
Bethink you, Cressida has known it too.
TROILUS: I remember, when I was a
   child
I used to take a boat, down at the shore,
And drift about on sleepy afternoons
Between the wrinkled windrows of the sea.

The sunshine veined the wave with seams of
    light
But there with naked summer on my back
I knew it was too happy to endure:
I knew that I was damned.

CRESSIDA: That's why I love you. Some day
I'll tell you about *my* private horrors. I've got some
beauties.

(But the liquor, blessed anodyne, is changing
the rhythm). What do I care for Troy fallen, or
risen either, he cries; or any other thing, now you're
here; you tangible. Let's go away together; now,
tonight. Pan says we can take his car.

No, darling; it just won't work. It'd be a wash-
out. You must have something to be faithful to;
that's the kind you are.

I can be faithful to you.

I'm not big enough. You know you'd never be
happy if you let them down.

TROILUS: They let *me* down; and I was
    up so high.
O, for a few unblemished blessed weeks
I knew things at their worth, and loved the
    world—
My horse, my dog, my sword, my every-
    thing—

The better for my ecstasy of you.
Laugh at me if you will:
Even in my wardrobe I would say:
I wore this when I last knew Cressida.

CRESSIDA: And after all this rich dis-
covery,
We now recant? So sorry for ourselves?

TROILUS: Forgive me. I guess I'm gibbering.

CRESSIDA: My blessed, when you know
a woman's heart
So easy to be wrung, you will not wring it.

They take a mutually propitiating drink. Here's
to Us!

CRESSIDA: Silly as it sounds, I've got my little job to do also. I don't know whether Daddy is
really sick or not, but I've got to find out; and maybe I can learn something about the Greek plans. The
Horse, for instance.

TROILUS: How long will you be gone?

CRESSIDA: Ten days, I should think. I can't
possibly stay longer than that, I haven't got clothes.

TROILUS: Well that's good to know.

CRESSIDA: Think how glad you'll be to see
Antenor.

TROILUS: Sure; and every time I see his

homely pan I'll think of the one who ransomed him. There's lots of you I haven't given names to yet. Here's something I never saw before: this little flattened hollow in your upper lip. Something ought to be done about that.

CRESSIDA: We could get over some of the ground now . . . and then we'd still have something to look forward to when I get back.

TROILUS: Since I'm responsible for delivering you, I'll take charge of the return trip too. Ten days' leave of absence, that's all you get. Understand?

CRESSIDA: Darling, you know I'll do my best.

TROILUS: I've brought you something as a pledge and a luck-piece.

He gives her a little ornament in gold and blue enamel.

O Troilus, it's your squadron-pin. I know how much that means to you.

It means Ten Days Leave. You swear?

I swear.

You can count them every day when you put it on. And if the Greeks make any difficulty about coming back, Zeusalmighty, I'll bring over the whole regiment and take you by force.

But tonight, she whispers, force won't be necessary.

XXI

TOO BRIGHT FOR MY EYES

THERE'S STILL HEAVY MORNING shadow inside the deep tunnelled gateway. Sentries on duty stand rigorously to attention as the taxicab rolls slowly in over the ancient cobbles. She is jolted against him.

Even the rough stones of the world, he whispers, throw you in my arms. Goodbye my precious.

They'll see—

Not till I acknowledge the salute.

The taxi breathes deep, its eager panting loudened in the vaulted arch. But for a moment the mumbling stir seems to shield them.

I've had no experience in saying goodbyes, he says, almost roughly, and swings open the door. He steps out and salutes the guard, who stand at ease. It seems rather terrible to see everything just as usual. The thick walls sweating in a humid air, the painted sentry-box, the same clump of wild flowers seeded by the wind on a projecting corbel, the spots of light on soldiers' fresh polished boots and buckles.

Has the Greek escort started yet? he asks.

Yes, Captain, says the sergeant. We got their bugle a couple of minutes ago.

Open up then.

Yes, sir.—The lady's luggage?

She has it with her.

Okay.

As they unfasten the huge bolts he leans into the cab. Both are pretending to study her suit-case. I'm glad it's such a small one, he says.

Just enough for ten days.

You look adorable in that tweed and jersey, he whispers. Don't change till you have to. Remember, everything you're wearing I helped you to put on.

Even the pin, she admits, showing it under the flap of her jacket.

The gate opens, a dazzling surge of sunlight floods the opening. Troilus nods to the troops and re-enters the car. The bugle gives its appointed signal; the guard present arms; the cab rolls out.

I'm sorry darling, she says; the sun was too bright for my eyes.

The Radio Voice—a bit late in arriving—dashes into the gateway with his mouthpiece on the end of a wire.

Morning, everybody. This is the Radio Voice of the *Evening Trojan,* always first in News, Editorials, Features, Advertisements. Folks while you're all enjoying your morning coffee I've been down here watching the big doings at the East Gate. It was arranged to take place very early to avoid any sort of public demonstration. Miss Cressida, escorted by Captain Troilus, is just leaving, and the Greek party, bringing Captain Antenor, is on its way over; they will meet and exchange between the lines. I've just been talking with Miss Cressida, I hoped she would say something personally into the mike, but she begged to be excused. Naturally she feels very deeply on this sensational occasion. I guess it's the first time in history a woman has been exchanged for a military captain, certainly it's a wonderful compliment and I ought to tell you that this afternoon's paper will have a feature article by our Miss Lyde on What This Means For the Future of Woman. Don't forget to buy your newspaper! Just a moment, folks, while I check up. . . .

(He pauses briefly to consult the sergeant)

This is the Radio Voice of the *Evening Trojan,* broadcasting from our historical East Gate where the great armistice exchange is taking place. Miss Cressida looks stunning in her going-away costume, and the sergeant on duty—what's your name, sergeant? They like to have names—Sergeant Teucer;

that's a good old Trojan family—Sergeant Teucer tells me there were a lot of bon voyage packages here for her, from some very smart addresses. Miss Cressida gave me a last interview for the *Evening Trojan*. She said "I am doing this for Troy and at the request of the War Council. I hope it is the first step toward the peace we all need. I'm sure the Greeks will treat me with every courtesy and I shall be back soon with good news." That's what we all hope. There's no doubt about it, the Greeks are just as fed up with fighting as we are.

Folks, they're off. I certainly wish I could ride with them in the cab, it certainly is a romantic moment, I'd like to know what they're saying to each other. It's a tough assignment for Captain Troilus, people in the know have been saying he has more than a little sentimental interest in Miss Cressida and I'd be the last to blame him. The cab is rolling past the Big Horse, you know the Greeks have moved it up close to the city, I can see Captain Troilus pointing it out to her. She acts as if she don't like the look of it, no wonder, it's an ugly monster. I wonder if those Europeans think they can scare us with a boogy like that?

I can see the Greeks coming over the hill. They're giving Captain Antenor a handsome send-off, he's in an open car with a Greek officer, and there's a cavalry escort with a flag of truce. Sergeant

Teucer tells me the Greek officer is Captain Diomedes, that's really dramatic, because as you know he and Captain Troilus are by no means buddies. You heard how Troilus hung it on him at Sarpedoni's. Boy, this is a thrilling sight, this is tops; I'm getting out my field glasses so I can give you all the local color. The Greeks have halted, Miss Cressida's car goes forward slowly to meet them. Wait till the dust clears away. . . . I can see Antenor, folks I can see Captain Antenor. He's getting out of the car. He favors his right leg a little but he looks to be okay. The two cars are side by side, Captain Troilus is getting out. I can see his hand on his revolver, I'll bet he's afraid of some trick, that boy's a soldier, he's not taking any chances. Diomedes is laughing, I don't see anything to laugh about. Troilus doesn't pay any attention to him, just ignores him completely. Troilus greets Antenor, they throw their arms about each other, gosh I bet they're glad to see themselves. Captain Troilus looks as though maybe he'd like to do some more arm-throwing but he and Miss Cressie are both very correct. Folks this is a high spot, get it. He gives Miss Cressida the military salute, and Captain Diomedes politely helps her into the Greek car. Diomedes bends over to talk to her—the cavalry form round. Now Diomedes is saying something to Troilus, I wish I could hear it, but Troilus high-hats him, pays no attention. He and Antenor both stand at salute while the Greeks —say, I bet they did that on purpose! The car and escort rushed off so fast they left our two standing in a cloud of dust. Typical Greek manners. Now Troilus shows Antenor into the other car, he speaks to the driver. They're coming back. I guess he's sore all right, he's coming like a bat out of—I mean he's driving very fast. . . .

If Ilium had been a lip reader he might have reported what Diomedes said: Now it's *my* turn for a dance.

XXII

HONORS IN ECONOMICS

Headquarters of the G.E.F. are on a knoll, and from Calchas's tent—open at one end against the autumn afternoon—we see a vista of other tents and, rising high in the distance, the walls and towers of Troy. Dr Calchas has already accumulated round him some of the equipment of an economic expert; filing cases and charts and a typewriter. He sits at a long table with enough papers and memoranda to keep him happy, and behind him hangs a huge graph showing the progress of the Siege during its ten years. It has zigzag lines in various colors; but the most conspicuous of them, which we may suppose to represent the trend of the Greek cause, shows at last a sharp rising slope. The deep gulf preceding its upward turn very likely symbolizes the quarrel between Achilles and Agamemnon, when Achilles was sulking. The chart is divided into vertical sections indicating the years 1194 B.C. down to 1185 B.C.

Outside the tent a sentry paces to and fro, passing at regular intervals. Cressida, still wearing the tweed-and-jersey, and the blue squadron-pin, is arguing with her father.

But Daddy, she says, I must.

I'm sorry, my dear. It's impossible.

I've been here a week already. I've got to get some more clothes.

That suit looks very well. I've heard any number of officers say how becoming it is. I don't like women who change their clothes all the time.

It was beastly of you to get me here on the pretext of being sick.

I *was* sick. My hay fever was terrible. That's one reason I tried to get you on the phone. I wanted you to bring my atomizer.

I'll go back and get it for you.

There were other reasons too. I thought I would tip off that old fool Pandarus to the real situation.

He's *not* an old fool. He's the wisest kindest dearest most understanding person in the whole world. He helped me when *you* left me on the beach. You'll never know what he's done for me.—Almost in tears, she gazes miserably out toward the distant silhouette of Troy.

Dr. Calchas pushes aside his papers, takes off his

spectacles, and becomes as annoying as only the fathers of daughters can.

Did you ever know me to do anything without having it all figured out beforehand? I tell you, Troy isn't healthy just now. What sort of a father would I be to let you go back to a town that's going to be wiped out.

That's all phooey. Why they've got the finest fighters in the world, they've got the Greeks paralyzed. Look at Hector and Paris and—and men like that. They can twist Greek spears in circles.

Even if they were acrobats and demigods they can't beat the laws of economics. Old pal Pandarus knows that. Would you be interested to know that years ago he transferred the bulk of his personal funds into Greek securities?

I don't care anything about that. I said I'd go back in ten days, and the Greeks gave their word of honor. It was in the treaty.

My dear child, to use your own expression, phooey. In war there's no such thing as a word of honor. It isn't recognized in international law.

Only in the laws of economics?

The only honor in economics is facts. Take a look at this chart. It shows the fluctuation of Greek and Trojan strength through the whole war. Military efficiency is based on four components: Man Power, Munitions, Food Supply, and Morale. Troy had all the best of it in the beginning. They had geography and strategy in their favor. But look at those lines representing Trojan resources. Man Power declining, Munitions declining, Food Supply way down, and now even their psychology is shot. The minute Cassandra started her pacifist demonstrations their morale was ruined.

That Calamity Jane, says Cressida scornfully. She's a joke, even in her own family. She's a witch.

She's a good statistician. Let me ask you one question. Have people been getting enough to eat in Troy?

Of course not. Demeter was angry, the goddess of corn.

Goddess of taxicabs! While the Trojans were praying to Demeter, the Greeks were blockading the Dardanelles and cut off the grain supply from the Black Sea. You can see it on the graph, here. The moment those two sets of lines crossed each other, Troy going down and Sparta coming up, the decision was certain. That was the night I packed up and left.

Calchas is interrupted by a powerful sternutation.

In such a hurry you forgot your atomizer, she says.

This does just as well, he remarks, taking a gas mask from a peg where also hang a cloak and a helmet.—The filter in the mask keeps out the pollen perfectly. Did you know that good old Uncle Pan has a factory on a neutral island that makes them for both sides? Smart, hey?

If you could see yourself you'd sooner sneeze. You look definitely pixie.

Now Cressida, be sensible. You remind me of your mother. Your friends across the way are going to get some surprises; you're well out of it.

What kind of surprises?

Surprising ones. Now I'll have to leave you a while, there's a gas drill to test the new chemical bombs and we'll all look like pixies. I've asked some of the officers to drop in here for tea afterward. That'll cheer you up.

I wonder, she says.

He hands her a sheet of paper. Here's the latest table of weighted index numbers, look it over while I'm out. It might put some ideas in your head.— And please remember (he says as he leaves) these Greeks are business men, not poets.

Cressida tosses away the index numbers, looks warily out of the tent, both at the open end and through the loose flaps at the rear. After a moment of uncertainty she calls :—

Sentry! O sentry!

A Greek soldier in classic armor appears at the

opening. He salutes. All present and correct, miss.

Cressida puts on her most blandishing air : Poor fellow, I'm afraid you're awfully warm out there.

It is a bit hot, miss.

I've got some nice cool lemonade in a thermos. I thought you'd like some.

I sure would. Thanks a lot.

Can you come in and enjoy it?

Sorry, orders is orders. I'll drink it here.

Well I want you to do something for me.

Anything in reason, miss.

While my father's out I'm going to take a nap. You see, some of the officers are coming in for tea and I want to be fresh.

Absolutely, that's what they like.

I mean, I want to be rested. Will you let down the flaps of the tent and keep an eye on the front so I won't be disturbed.

Sure thing. Nothing easier. I won't let nobody bother you, if it was old Many-louse himself.

Left alone, she throws the army cloak around her and puts on the helmet. Looking at herself she observes that her stockings and slippers betray her; then notices that in a corner of the tent are her father's riding boots. She slips into them. Cautiously she peers through the flaps at the back of the tent, then retreats quickly as if alarmed.

There is a furtive scratching against the rear

canvas; she shrinks behind the table in dismay. A gauntleted arm comes groping through and a figure garbed much like herself slips in. It is wearing a similar long cloak and helmet, the face is hidden by a gas mask. Her first impulse is to call for help, but the attitude of the other is curiously timid. She bends over the table and pretending to be occupied with the papers keeps her face concealed.

The stranger salutes, stands evidently puzzled by her disregard, then moves slowly forward trying to see her face. As if absorbed in study she keeps always averted. He tries, by repeated saluting, to get her attention. At last he makes a mumbling sound through the mask. Still there is no answer, so removing one gauntlet he draws a scroll from under his cloak and holds it out toward her. She looks sideways at it, and sees that his hand is black.

Fuscus!

He tears off his mask.

Gemini Pollux, it's Miss Cressie. Zeusalmighty, I feared maybe you wuz Colonel Ash-heels.

How you frightened me! It's a good thing you took off your glove.

Nigger always forgets he black all over. O lawd, O lawd, what a conniption.

What's this, asks Cressida, looking at the scroll.

Dat aint nothin', just some ole Greek writin' fo' camouflage. No ma'am, dis is de importance.

He takes a small folded paper, rather damp, from inside his helmet.

I'm sorry ef it aint very savory. Dat aint just perspiration, dat's fright.

We hear dese Europeans gwine do gas drill, I figure I could masquerade myself across. Co'se Marse Trolius couldn't come so I volunteer. It's dat nobility obliege dey alluz talk about. Quality fall in love it sho' make anxiety fo' de servants.

But Cressida is reading her letter and doesn't hear him. He tiptoes across and looks out of the front of the tent.

Holy cat, dese folks look ominous. See dat great big grub-wagon. I don't like de look o' dem big shootin' irons. Miss Cressie, you better come along home wid me. I don' feel to linger roun' here. What-all you doin' in dat Amazon garbage?

She has read the letter.

My darling. How is he?

He fightin' mighty smart, he lay out Greeks like fish on a slab, but I reckon he pretty low in his mind. He certainly count on dat ten-day limit.

I'll write him a note for you to take.

Dere's one thing, Miss Cressie, ef you'll take off yo' helmet. He ask me special to report on yo' eyebrows.

We'll have to hurry. There are some officers

coming in here for tea. I was just trying to escape myself when you came.

You come along wid me, back to de ole home grounds.

We'd both be caught. I haven't anything to hide my face.

You take dis mask and sneak off. I'll stay here an' serve 'em tea.

But as he says this there are several heavy bangs outside, as of a rifle-butt hammered on a wooden platform. The voice of the sentry calls: Are you all right, miss?——And at the sound, Fuscus is already almost half way through the other side of the tent.

All right, sentry, she says.

I thought I heard you asking for something.

Just reading to myself. Please don't disturb me again.

Okay, miss.

Fuscus, terrified, comes back a little way. Honey, he whispers, I guess you're right. Dese folks is too nervous for good company.

Listen to me carefully, she says. I'm writing a note, but I daren't go into details. Tell him to look out. The Greeks are planning something big. I don't know what, but something terrible. I don't even know if they'll let me come back as they promised.

Dat's bad, moans Fuscus. Dat aint honorable.

Tell him I love him and I'm doing my best. Tell him you saw me wearing this.——She shows the blue pin, and hastily finishes the message. Fuscus, again going carefully to look out of the back flaps, is horrified by a bugle call and distant heavy gunfire.

Dere goes dat ole afternoon barrage. Dat don't sound congenial.

Hurry, she says.

He puts the note in his helmet, adjusts the gas mask, and is gone through the back of the tent.

But an hour later, pouring tea (Dr Calchas's papers have been carefully moved to one end of the table) she has changed her clothes and her mood too. The Greek officers are gallantly attentive; especially Diomedes. Calchas, sitting on the camp bed with Agamemnon and Menelaus, manages to keep the two generals occupied with diagrams and reports, but the younger men are standing close round Cressida. Achilles, Nestor, Ajax and Ulysses keep jostling for preferred position; Diomedes however has established himself firmly at her left side—— where he does not interfere with the tea-pouring and has proximity for intimate asides.

For General Agamemnon, she says. He takes two lumps. Don't you think I'm clever to know that already?

You're a quick learner, says Diomedes. He hands the cup to Ajax, repeating: For General Agamemnon. Ajax, surprised into accepting it, tries to work the same manoeuvre on Ulysses. Sure, for General Agamemnon, says Ulysses; over there. Ajax has to take it to the General, and Ulysses moves into the vacated position.

Two? she asks Ulysses brightly. Think of being able to have all the sugar you want. In Troy, nobody gets more than one. I suppose it's good for the figure.

You don't need to worry, is everybody's thought; but Diomedes says it first.—There's lots of things you can get here you couldn't get in Troy, he adds.

Especially cucumber sandwiches, she says. Major Nestor, why don't you pass them round.

Yes, for goodness sake, give the girl elbow room, Achilles grumbles; and takes Nestor's place at her right as the old man obediently chases the tray of sandwiches.

This is the way to make a war worth while, says Ajax. Why didn't we think of it sooner?

DIOMEDES: I've been thinking of it right along.

ULYSSES: When I get back to Ithaca I'm going to serve tea every afternoon.

It won't be long now, says Nestor, trying to

push his way back to Cressida, with the sandwiches as excuse.

How about some sandwiches over here, calls Menelaus, who is bored with Calchas's palaver. Nestor ungraciously complies.

We'll miss the good old war when it's over, remarks Diomedes. You better make the most of it while it lasts.

You're not making yourself useful, she replies. Give this cup to my father.—Colonel Achilles, you don't take any sugar, do you.

ACHILLES: You're wonderful. How did you know?

CRESSIDA: Don't you remember, you told me about the arthritis in your heel?—Now is everybody served?

DIOMEDES: Everybody except you. Have a cucumber sandwich. (He has handed the other cup to Nestor, and captured the tray.)

CRESSIDA: If you all stand so close I can't pour.

ACHILLES: I'm afraid the boys forget their manners. It's so long since they had any feminine society.

CRESSIDA: Except at Sarpedoni's.

DIOMEDES: That's not society. That's just gymnastics.

AJAX: It's a pity Miss Cressida isn't twins.

ACHILLES: Don't bring that up.

CRESSIDA: It's very sweet of you all to be so flattering. I shall be quite sorry when I have to go.

(*There's a brief embarrassed pause*)

DIOMEDES: When you really get to know us, you won't want to go.

AJAX: Are second cups allowed?

CRESSIDA: Yes indeed. I'm sure you're all thirsty after your hard work. What sort of drill was it today, I heard such unpleasant noises?

ACHILLES: Don't let's talk shop. You know, I'd almost forgotten women wore such pretty clothes.

DIOMEDES: He'd forgotten they wore them at all.

CRESSIDA: If you're rude to each other I'll go and talk to the generals.

AJAX: Diomedes is sore because you didn't bring your little friend with you, what's her name?

CRESSIDA: Antigone. Isn't she darling.

NESTOR: Then we could have some dancing. (He is still trying to find a way through the fringe of elbows).

DIOMEDES: We'll have some dancing anyhow.

ULYSSES: I know what kind of a dress that is, it's a cocktail chiton.

DIOMEDES: It's the kind of thing you wear when you feel reckless, isn't it?

ULYSSES: Penelope used to have one like that, back home.

ACHILLES: But not as pretty.

CRESSIDA: I think I'd better go back and fetch Antigone. Don't you think I'm a bit outnumbered?

DIOMEDES: The Trojans don't appreciate you, darling, or they'd never let you go.

ACHILLES: Forget about the Trojans, they're in the bag.

AJAX: Don't you think our uniforms are much handsomer than theirs?

But Agamemnon and Menelaus have had all they can endure of Calchas.

I don't think it's right to let you young fellows monopolize the only lady, says Agamemnon, coming over.

I quite agree, complains old Nestor.

We're very grateful to you, continues the commander-in-chief, for giving us a softening influence. It isn't good for these boys to be away from home so long.

It isn't good for anyone, grumbles Menelaus.

They're a little rough sometimes, but I'm sure their intentions are good, says Agamemnon.

The very best, assents Diomedes.

Time for evening inspection, Agamemnon announces. On duty, gentlemen.

With polite salutes, all retire; but Diomedes lingers a moment after the others.

I thought you might like to have this back, before anyone else sees it. He hands her a paper: she recognizes the note she wrote for Troilus.

Better destroy it, he suggests.

For a moment she cannot speak.——The slave? she asks.

We stopped him, of course. This is an army camp, not a rural free delivery.

I mean——is he——

He's all right. In the usual way, he'd have been tortured, but I got him off. He's lucky.

That was good of you.

I'm always good. I can prove it. . . . Now listen, lovely, don't spoil that pretty face with tears. Maybe you're lucky too. We'll talk about that later.

XXIII

HEROISM OF UNCLE PAN

O nerve of thought, alert, aware,
That strips the moment naked-bare
And lives in double: Here, and There.
            TROILUS: *A Song in Absence*

Pandarus has heroisms too. He
has persuaded Troilus to spend this evening at Sarpedoni's; and the boy has not been good company
lately.

Old Soapy welcomes them effusively, for business is poor. The orchestra works diligently, the
Sanskrit chippendales are deployed to every advantage, but it is only too evident that there are no cus-
tomers on the Greek side of the house. Some Trojan
burghers are enjoying the Pelagian Plate and the
Drachma Dinner (Sarpedoni has ways of evading
the Food Control) but the dancers are few. Antigone
and Deiphobus have the floor almost to themselves;
occasionally joined by Paris with either Chryseis or
Briseis, we are not sure which (nor does it matter).

The twins are in an alcove with Paris and Antenor, but Antenor's recent wound prevents him from dancing. He makes up for it on the settee.

Good evening, my lord; good evening, Prince Troilus, says Sarpedoni. Mighty glad to see you, gentlemen. You haven't been here since that night we had the little disturbance. That was quite an outbreak of high spirits, wasn't it. Over in the quiet corner? Certainly, certainly.

Not much disturbance tonight, remarks Pandarus.

Things have been very quiet. I think the Greeks must have been put within bounds. They haven't been here at all the past few evenings.

Better slip over and see old man Agamemnon, Pandarus suggests. Maybe he needs some baksheesh.

Old Soapy manages a laugh. It seems such a pity, he says; there's a whole new lot of Personals on the bulletin board. Some of them very attractive, too. Would the Prince care to go and look them over?

Troilus makes a sombre wave of distaste.

I'll send you a cocktail while you're studying the menu. Oysters are in again now.

No cocktail, Troilus says. Lemon squash.

Send two anyhow, says Pandarus. If he doesn't want it, I do.

Tomorrow is Ten Days. That's cocktail enough

for me. The last time I was here, she sat over there. Hey, Sarpedoni! Turn up the chairs at that table, don't let anyone sit there.

Certainly, sir, agrees Sarpedoni, always eager to please.

Now, my dear boy, you must buck up. We can't go on like this. Ask Antigone for a dance, make Deiphobus work for his fun. The little minx, I didn't think she had it in her.

When we were here before, I was making *you* dance. Remember that dress she wore?—What the Hades did you bring me here for; I'm going uptown to the dog chariot.

Troilus, please, Pandarus begs, pulling him down. Here are the ambrosias. Drink one, for my sake. Come on now, we'll drink her health.

They do so. The loveliest creature Zeus ever made, Troilus murmurs.

Sorry I'm so goofy, he says presently; but I'm living in two places at once: Here, and There. My mind is over in that damned Greek camp, wondering what she's doing, saying, wearing, thinking, how those bloody Spartans are behaving to her, what she's trying to tell me—and why haven't I heard from her? Not one word.

You know perfectly well, they wouldn't let her write. After all you haven't got much longer to wait.

How do I know she'll come back? Fuscus hasn't.
Poor old coon, I suppose I sent him to his death.
Zeusalmighty, how I hate myself.

Obviously they caught him and put him behind
a nice wire fence. He's all right, he didn't care much
for fighting anyhow.

Pan, you don't know what it's like to be torn in
two like this.

Go and tear those twins in two. Have a dance,
forget yourself for a few minutes.—Pandarus
catches Antigone's eye, and signals to her for help.

Nothing is real any more, the boy groans. Only
memory. When I come off duty I just hang about
Epsilon Street and look up at her windows; the same
window she stood at. I see the flowers in your garden, like little safety valves where the world blows
off all its color and beauty—doesn't anybody *know*
how the world is packed and bursting with loveliness?—and where is *she*, the one who made it beautiful? What do you *do* about that sort of thing?

Pandarus knows—no one better—there is nothing to be done, except order another ambrosia.

Write poetry, he suggests. I remember when
Ianthe Hellespont and I—

Of course I've done that, Troilus interrupts. But
it kind of fades out when you've no one to share it
with.—Do you know what was the last thing she
said to me when she left?

Goodbye?

Too bright for my eyes. It's exactly what she is.
There's an omen in it. My radiant shining creature,
too bright for my eyes. I wrote a verse about it,
would you like to hear it?

Even this, perhaps, Uncle Pan would have suf-
fered, but just then Antigone and Deiphobus join
them.

Take this boy out and get his mind off his
troubles, Pan says to her.

You can shut your eyes and pretend it's Cressida, she offers.

You'll have to shut your ears too, says Deiphobus. Hey, chatterbox?

That'll do from you, says Antigone. Troilus,
why haven't you been up to the apartment?

I didn't have the heart. Besides, every time I
asked the doorman, he said Deiphobus was there.—
What do you suppose she's wearing this evening?
That tweed and jersey thing?

Not at night, I hope, Antigone says. I'll bet
they're giving her a swell party, this is her last night
over there.

I hope so. I mean, I hope it's her last night.

Come and dance and we'll talk about it.

You do smell rather like her, he admits as they
swing off on the floor.

It's the same perfume.

How are things, Deiphobus asks Pandarus.

Not good.

Troilus looks a bit mouldy, poor kid. He hasn't even finished his drink. (Which Deiphobus does for him).

Yes, he's badly cut up. Try to pull him out of it.

That girl certainly knocked him for a row of pylons. Remember the old folk-tale: Once upon a girl there was a time.

My fault, too, in a way. I thought they'd both take it in their stride.

Troilus hasn't got any stride. He takes everything in convulsions.—She'll never come back, will she?

I doubt it.

I was just thinking, you might fix it for me to take over the lease of that apartment. I wouldn't want little Tig to be lonely.

I don't like anybody to be lonely; and there's really no reason why they should be.

Pan, you're a swell egg. Have a drink on me.

You're very kind. Thank you. And after that I was rather thinking of asking one of those clerical twins for a dance. I think I've earned some relaxation.

It's a good idea; but those girls aren't relaxation. —Where do you suppose the damned Spartans are keeping themselves?

Sarpedoni says they haven't been here several evenings.

There's funny stuff going on over there. Our intelligence department reported something queer this afternoon. They've got all their work companies down on the beach overhauling the ships. What do you suppose that means?

Sending back for reinforcements?

I was wondering, do you suppose they're getting ready to quit?

Extraordinary. Surely not.

They haven't been very active in the field lately; not since the exchange of prisoners. Hector had a queer hunch: he thought maybe they were going back home and take Cressida with them, to even up for Helen.

Zeusalmighty; if that happens Troilus will follow up with a ten-year Siege of Sparta. . . .

The music stops suddenly, and the Radio Voice, much amplified, booms across the hall:—

S.O.S. . . . S.O.S. . . . This is an emergency broadcast. Excuse my interrupting you, folks, but this is an emergency. Calling all troops. Calling all troops, by order of King Priam. Mysterious activity has been noted in the Greek camp; no reason for alarm, folks, but army headquarters wishes to be prepared for any eventuality. All leave is cancelled at once, officers and men report to quarters. Civilians are ad-

) 220 (

vised to return inside the walls. This emergency broadcast will be repeated at intervals of three minutes. All officers and men report to quarters at once.

Thank you, my lord, thank you, says Sarpedoni as Pandarus leaves in perfect dignity, monocle brightly polished.

Sorry to go so early, Pandarus regrets. But I suppose patriotism—

Just so, my lord. Some of the officers left so promptly they forgot to pay their checks.

And I didn't even get my dance, Uncle Pan reflects.

XXIV

ARMY SUPPLIES, RUSH

T HE SAME EVENING: IN FACT, just about the time Troilus is asking Antigone what Cressida might be wearing, she's putting it on. It's the prickly pear, of course; poor dear, there's no alternative.

She's taking her time over it. No matter how late D. is (she thinks of him by initial only) she intends to keep him waiting. In the curtained corner allotted for her privacy she can't help hearing the unusual bustle of the camp tonight. There's a stealthy but continuous movement of troops, and a feeling of things about to happen. Calchas is off at a staff meeting, she is alone in the tent, but the sentry's pace is regular outside.

As she fastens the blue pin at her breast she wonders how she will feel when she unpins it; for of course her mind is already made up. She is writing a sort of letter in her mind. People who are slow to intimate speech compose many such. Partly to Troilus, partly to herself :—

My darling dear, you're sweet. I've just put on your pin, it made me think of tarnished cream. My sweet. We had such a lot of good laughs together. There never was anyone like you. The feeling of this camp tonight makes me as nervous as a witch, something's happening, I can't find out what. I'm as good as a prisoner here. My darling I know you're counting minutes till tomorrow, I can't help myself. Maybe I'll get back somehow; I'll get back when I can. All this doesn't really count, I've got my fingers crossed, it's just an accident. I will try, I *did* try. You know I'm your girl. I did mean to be faithful; what a ridiculous word. I guess I'm just not that way by nature. I wish I had your lovely words to make me strong. If we'd had more time you'd have made me someone quite different. Beauty never guessed before. What does it matter, anyway? Blessed boy, nothing can ever spoil those times we had. O please be careful, these Greeks are as hard as nails; I'm so frightened of what may happen, they've got it all on a chart. If I'm nice to D. maybe he'll tell me about the Horse and I can warn them. . . .

I suppose you have to be faithful to someone, sooner or later. Later. I wonder if D. would be a good one to be faithful to. Probably not. I could try. How different he is, the big roughneck; but he's rather sweet too. He's been nice in his way. He doesn't *need* me, like you do, poor darling, but he certainly wants me. He'd be rather cute when you really got him down. I wonder what Uncle Pan would think, bless and damn his old heart. I guess he'll never forgive me. Yes he will, Uncle Pan will forgive anything. He has to, the old rascal. . . .

That was the real me, my sweet, the person you loved. My darling, he's such a believing soul, and I'm breaking down everything he trusts. O if you could come this minute and tell me about things. I didn't want you to love me. Come with that regiment and take me by force. . . .

Are you there? calls Diomedes, entering the main part of the tent. He is carrying a cocktail shaker of classic form.

Certainly I'm here. No chance to be anywhere else.

Sorry if I'm late.

Are you? she says calmly. I didn't notice. You can't be too late for me.

He grins to himself. He knows how important it is to a woman to keep up her self-esteem.

Big doings tonight, he says. It took some smart finagling to get time off.

I thought things sounded lively. What's going on?

Just landing supplies, he says cannily. Come on out; you must be fixed up by now.

Take your time, Big Boy.

I got the canteen to shake up a Grecian Urn, that's our favorite in the officers' mess. I thought we might have a snort for luck.

Good idea, we'll probably need it.——She emerges from behind the curtain, beautiful indeed.

Chersonesus! he exclaims in admiration. That dress is gorgeous.

I'm glad you like it. It's all I've got.

It's more than you need, but it'll do for a while.

I hope we're going out. I've been cooped up in this tent until I'm crazy.

We sure are. All out.

Let's go and have dinner at the Horse.

At the Horse? What do you mean?

That big Horse I'm always hearing about. It's a night club, isn't it?

For Pete's sake, where did you get that idea? That's rich! Why the Horse is a——don't let's get technical. It's hell on roller skates.

I'm disappointed.

We'll go to the officers' club, they've got music there, and then back to my tent. I told your old man not to be worried, I'd be responsible for you.

I hope you meant it.

He has poured the cocktails. Here's hoping, he says.

Why all the sudden excitement, she asks.

It's not sudden. I've been excited about you ever since Sarpedoni's.

I don't mean romantic excitement. I mean military.

We were waiting for the equinox; that's tonight. Equinox is always lucky. Do you know why? That's when night becomes more important than day.

He is in a mood to offer endearments, but she evades.

Baby girl, you look good enough to eat. Do you love me?

I don't dislike you.

That's awfully negative. You know there's one thing about you I don't like. That Trojan pin. Do you think it's tactful to wear that around here?

You're the expert on tact, she says; satirically but also in a tone of provocation.

How about taking it off?

No. It was given to me.

I'll give you something better instead.

I like this one.

Our regimental badge is much handsomer. We used to collect this kind in baskets, after a good day in the field.

It's not so! You're making that up.

Maybe I am. It's fun, making up to you. Come on, let's get rid of it.

No, this dress really needs it. It's cut rather low.

I see it is. Well, if it's part of your fixings, I'm being premature. I thought it was just sentimental.

Perhaps it is.

Listen honey, let's pass up the stuffing and carve turkey. Quit fretting about the old home town. Troy's in for a bad run of dice. You've got all the dope on that chart, right in front of you. See that line shooting up to the top? That's your friend Diomedes.

You're a good salesman.

Why not? I've got something to sell.

You're so different, she murmurs half to herself; sadly and yet also somehow fascinated. So terribly different!

What's that? Now baby girl, don't be blue. I know it's tough, but we won't make it any better by moping. You've cut your cable, now you've got clear sailing. We'll make a fresh start. You haven't begun to live yet, I can see it in your eye.

How can you; I'm not even looking at you.

But you will, because you're sweet. Awfully sweet . . . and soft . . . and lonely . . . and chock full of dynamite. You will . . . won't you?

And she does.

You said you'd be kind to me, she falters.

Watch me. And before we go out and have fun, let's get this clear. Troy's washed out.

I suppose so.

We'll have a drink on it.—And there's nobody in Troy you're tied up with. Is there?

Not any more.

And you know whose girl you are now, so that's settled. Nothing to worry about. All hunkydory. Stencilled G.E.F., Army Supplies, Rush.

Where's that cocktail, she says, reaching for it blindly. Can we go somewhere where we won't need to think?

And remember this camp is full of woman-tamers out of work. Don't pay attention to any of 'em.

O damn you, she bursts out, I'm sold, now shut up. . . . Better not try to make me love you, I might be so everlasting faithful you'd never get rid of me.

He is puzzled, but expertly interested. He holds the cocktail glass to her lips as though it were medicine.

You'd never break your heart over anyone, would you, she says finally.

I wouldn't need to.—What say we get started? I've got a date with some of your Trojan friends to-morrow.

Tomorrow?

We're going to pull off a nice little skirmish, just to keep them from brooding.

No, don't let them brood, she says cryptically. —Come on, Big Boy, where's that place where there's music?

XXV

THE DOOM TAKES CHARGE

Now is the sun in Libra; time suspends on balance; the starry scales at poise.

Such days have been; will be again. Light streams through sure mutations, never perceived until too late. First fanned in gilt above the scarps of Ida; meridian, white and sheer; bent later in false purple on the barren sea. Then westering sails, trimming their wind for Tenedos, cut black against the glare.

Light and darkness, our only gods, wash the world in beauty.

It streams past Troilus unheeded. Wide spreads the familiar view. There are the rocky mountain glades where the sudden snake trickles downhill. There are the rivers of boyhood with their bladed reeds. There the trampled field, the Greek tents dingy with weather, the monstrous effigy leering against the wall. We hadn't realized it's so big. The head rears above the lower rampart, stares into the city with blank makebelieve eyes.

And the mind pours by. Thought, in which the heavy world floats lighter than bubble, metronomes a dull and groping swing: beauty to horror and back and again; and all the joys and ribaldries between. Thought, which shames at nothing; denies nothing; affirms nothing. Awareness only, clear and cold, and the slow corruption of the hours.

He is on the wall, watching.

I think I see her, he exclaims for the twentieth time.—Is that her?

Uncle Pan has joined his vigil occasionally, but is too nervous to stay long. He finds it difficult to talk.

There's a car coming by Scamander Parkway, Troilus suggests hopefully. But surely they'd give her an escort?

Only a taxi, going down to Sarpedoni's, Uncle Pan observes. But my dear boy, there's a thousand things might have prevented her. Her father's illness, maybe; or very likely the Greeks simply wouldn't let her.

She said she'd come, and she will, Troilus insists. Of course she couldn't get across this morning; there was fighting in the way. But this afternoon things have been pretty quiet.

Too quiet, I don't like the look of it.

Hector's taken his troop down across the river to see what's going on.

Isn't that Horse nearer than it was, Pandarus asks? I've always laughed at the thing, but great Pluto, I don't like it sticking its head right over the wall.

Troilus is so busy visualizing a beloved figure in tweed and jersey he scarcely pays attention.

You know (Pandarus says) Cressida had a queer dream about that Horse one time . . . did she tell you?

No. What? The Horse? If she doesn't get back by dark I'll take a squad and chop the damn thing up. Make a bonfire of it to light her home. Say, why didn't I think of that before? Of course she won't come by daylight, she wouldn't want a lot of publicity and people staring at her. You know how she hates crowds.

Most likely her father would keep her until after dinner anyway, he adds presently. They probably have better grub than we do.

And later still he says: I wonder if I counted the days wrong? Did she say *after* Ten Days, or on the Tenth Day?

Pandarus is silent. The light slopes lower now, troublesome to looking. The sunset breeze, more softly moving, lets down its casual scents: the acids

of the beach, the dry pollen of the dunes. It spar-
kles on the riverside willows, bends the grasses
nearer. What way did you come, sweet air, and
bring no news?

Even the wind is coming from her direction,
Troilus mutters. His hand by chance at his face, he
catches the taint of metal on his fingers.

I tried to keep her sweetness on my hands, he
cries furiously.

There drifts a waft of sour burning from the
Greek rubbish pits. And in the smoky haze beyond
the river, shouts and the jangle of cavalry gear.

Here comes Hector and his troop, he says eagerly. They'll tell us if they've seen anything.

Let's go down to the Cerberus and have some
coffee, urges Pandarus. (The Cerberus is the lunch-
wagon just inside the gate, first resort of troops coming off duty). We can come back here later.—He
tries to draw him away. But Troilus is leaning excit-
edly over the parapet.

Wait a minute! Look! Zeusalmighty, they're
laughing, they're cheering, waving to us! They've
had good luck; gemini, they've got a whole wagon-
load of trophies. They've captured a Spartan flag.
Just look at Hector's face, there's good news!

He runs along the rampart, stumbles down the
steps in a rush, to meet Hector in the great archway.

Hullo, kid; you should have been with us, Hector says. He grins down from horseback, flushed and sweaty. They're licked. They're getting aboard the ships, they're quitting. What do you think of that?

Such shouts of triumph from the gathering crowd, Troilus can't ask his question. Hector waves a battered helmet for silence.

We had a smart little scrap down by the ford, but I think they were only bluffing. Trying to screen the retreat. Every time we really went at 'em, they broke.

The crowd applauds noisily, but Hector sees Troilus beseeching to be heard, clutching his saddle-cloth. He supposes it's the boy's disappointment not to have been with them.

Too bad you missed it, old man, he says kindly. I nearly trimmed your friend Diomedes. He was too slick, he got away, but I sliced off a piece of his armor. Just happened to catch him across the joint. He seemed sort of dopy, I guess he must have been on a party last night. How's this for a souvenir?

From his belt he detaches a curved bronze and leather breastplate, dulled and hammered by long service. Troilus takes it in his hands. He sees, what Hector had not even noticed: to the collar is fastened his own blue pin.

Stick it up in the messroom, says Hector easily; it'll look good in the showcase. I'll go on and clean up.

Hoofs on cobbles, the troop push off, the crowd follow with cheers. Even the sentries are off for a drink; this is no moment for discipline. Troilus and Uncle Pan are left; the boy still dumbly holding the broken relic. He knows now.

He turns the metal shard, examining it with professional attention. Good workmanship, he says. That's a grand piece of bronze. Rippled to turn off a spear-point. I guess it's turned off too many. See how cleverly that leather lining is rivetted in?

He breaks into queer laughter. Uncle Pan is frightened by something dead in the voice, and looks closer, curiously. Troilus tries to hide the badge, but Pan has seen. They look at each other.

Shall we put it in the showcase, Troilus says; still with that stranger's laugh. And then, gravely, disdainfully: Too rich an armor for his mongrel heart. He tosses the breastplate into a stone corner, where it falls with a clang.

Uncle Pan, his usual wisdom broken by pity, damns Cressida foully with an oath. But Troilus, who seems in that moment the older man, silences him with a touch :—

I can't unlove her now.

Just inside the great gate is an old bench. He sits there quietly; where he has so often paused, exhausted and happy, coming in from the field. Uncle

Pan, though helpless to comfort, will not leave him. From the distance, the rising murmur and stir of a town in jubilee. Through a loudspeaker in the shadows of the gate the Radio Voice booms out :—

. . . Just about the biggest night little old Troy town ever had. Everyone in the studio is so excited I can hardly speak. There'll be an extra on the streets shortly, meanwhile I'll try to give you the picture. Folks, this is official. The rumor that's been going round ever since last night is positively confirmed. The Greeks have quit. Those Europeans have had enough. Folks, you'll have to pardon me if I'm a bit incoherent, but we've won the War. As a matter of fact we've been practically certain of it here in the *Trojan* office for quite some days, we had a front page all set up yesterday, but we weren't going to spill it until we got a release from the War Office. O boy, O boy, what a night this is going to be.

Folks, we suspected the end was near when the Greeks asked for a truce a fortnight back and made that exchange of prisoners. But today they just walked out and left us without any good old war on our hands. They've already embarked a large number of their soldiers, they set sail from the Marine Terminal without any special secrecy, they're smart enough to know when they're licked. This afternoon we captured some of their men who admit it. By sunset some of their ships were already beyond Tenedos. Good riddance, what? Colonel Hector and his troop were out scouting this afternoon and drove back enemy outposts who were trying to cover the retreat. The Greeks showed every sign of demoralization, some of them even threw down their weapons and ran. Our boys came back with a whole truckload of arms and armor as trophies. I guess you can hear the reception our men are getting: the crowd wouldn't let them return to barracks but forced them to ride up the Avenue under a blizzard of ticker tape. Folks the old town's gone haywire. We've just had a flash, they're starting a bonfire in the plaza in front of the Palladium. Dean Laocoon and Princess Cassandra tried to calm them but the people are crazy with enthusiasm, they wouldn't listen. Some of them are talking about getting up moonlight parties to go and see the battlefields, No Man's Land and the trenches; I guess that can wait for daylight, but some romantic thrill to see the spot where Achilles pitched his tent! It's a fact, folks, they say the Greek camp is almost empty already; they've burned a lot of their supplies and left half their equipment—including the famous Horse. What a laugh that was! The boys in the office say there's a movement on foot to tear an opening in the wall so they can drag in the Horse and put it in the plaza as a victory monument. Sorry, I'm coughing,

I'm hoarse myself—I know that's terrible, but anything goes on a night like this. I'll sign off for a while to get the latest dope for you. We're taking a mike up on the *Trojan* tower, they've got the big searchlight up there, we can see everything. Remember, full details in your favorite paper, first in peace as well as war, and in News, Editorials, Features, Advertisements. . . .

Troilus rises, looks carefully over his equipment.
She may still be there, he says.
Troilus, don't be mad, says Uncle Pan in horror.
Has everyone forgotten her except me?
They've taken her in the ships.
Maybe they have. They haven't taken Diomedes.
Uncle Pan tries weakly to hold him. Troilus pushes him aside.
I said I'd make a bonfire to light her home.
But what are you going to do?
Get the squadron. They'll go with me.

Cassandra appears in the shadows.
CASSANDRA: Stay him not, my lord. He's
    happy now:
The waiting's over and the doom takes charge.
  PANDARUS: It's too horrible. He loved her
so. He had just learned how life is sweet.

) 238 (

CASSANDRA: What better hour to leave it?
It was beautiful and it is ended.
And Troy itself that blazes high tonight
Stands on the cope of being.
PANDARUS: What's the good of winning the
whole War if we lose *him?* He's worth a thousand
Cressidas.

CASSANDRA: Nay, he made her in his
mind
To loveliness; and let her so remain.
He made himself the finer, thinking so.
I speak not for ourselves, but for The Wis-
dom
That sees the world in pattern and in fable.
Our misery and horror that impend
It purges, in due time, to fairy-tale.
The very legend that men misremember
Shall be more true than truth.
It gives us inlook to a better good,
The ghost creative that works fitfully
And finds no perfect thing.
PANDARUS: But it *was* perfect. I know more
about that sort of thing than you do, and I tried to
make them happy. I love them both.

CASSANDRA: Be glad then, for their sake.
She was, for him, The Wisdom.
She gave, unargued, her bliss absolute:
She taught the sting and honey of desire,

The necessary laughters, large and small;
Unwitting, taught him to approach the
    world
As lover does his woman. In that mood,
That vision, and that kindness, we pre-
    vail. . . .

XXVI

THE BRUTE IS PAST CONTROL

Equo ne credite, Teucri.
—AENEID, II, 48

IT IS STILL THE GATEWAY, IN THE gloom; and these two, Pandarus and Cassandra—the kind and silly flesh, the hard purity of reason—watchful in the sentry niches at each wing. And through the arch of shadow we look out into clear night.

The gate's open, says Uncle Pan, incredulous.

I opened it myself, she answers. It saves trouble.

Her voice has a new authority; even a new eagerness. The long disbelief will soon be ended. (Will she, in the hands of Agamemnon, be less priestess and more woman?)

Outside there grows a queer deep humming fluttering sound, rumbled compressions chanting of escape; menacing but almost soothing too.

The damned Horse is purring, Pan suggests.

) 241 (

Try to believe (Cassandra says) this is not agony,

But work of art accomplished.

Power, the useful brute, is past control.

This sounds like terrible nonsense to Uncle Pan, but he is aware, vaguely, that articulate sound is only an outer skin of meaning.—From the darkness of the bay, off Sigeum, a rocket streams in golden pencil-curve. Slowly it floats and sinks.

A shooting star, he cries.

A signal, she says; and on her word the horrid siren. Distant at first, it rises to a whinnying shriek. It might be thought the neighing of an incredible Horse: a trumpeting screaming mockery of cruelty and pride. It shreds the innocent dark like a howling shell, a falling bomb. It bursts in rolling thunders of convoluted shock.

And the night is in motion. Now there is no softness of sweet shrubs and beachy smells but a putrid gas of burning and masked figures that have crept through the fields rise from darkness with blurred unhuman faces goggled and snouted like foxes, horses, beetles, like the insect troops of horror that Troilus foresaw. Pandarus reels and recoils in his corner; Cassandra proud and pale, unmoved.

Just a minute folks, bawls the Radio Voice (a little cracked with disbelief) everything okay, we're up here on the tower where we can see everything, some of the boys are a bit wild tonight, I'll just plant the searchlight right on the Gate so we can see what's going on.

A shaft of chalky dazzle seems to rend the gateway : or has it been torn apart by some fantastic explosion? For what we see over the dissolving wall is the pale Horse, terrific. The whole archway is now just the loom of its forelegs under the arched and barrelled chest. It has grown like a dream in the darkness of a lonely mind, like impossible foul fungus against the rotting wall; as beautiful and dire. It towers enormous: down into the city (our own Troy) it glares in gloried lust, the grinning jowl, the grated teeth, the flattened ears; and the round blank balls of eyes are makebelieve no longer but clear and burning and shoot radials of light. The mouth is a machine gun and the tubed and rifled nostrils are pipes of searing flame.

A long stricken hush, then the city behind us (Troy, our own) breaks to panic frenzy, police siren and bugle cry, fire whistle and motor horn, the tankle-tonk of the junkman's cowbells, the shatter of million panes of glass.

Just a minute folks, yells the Radio Voice, something's gone wrong, hold everything. It looks like a seven-alarm fire, they must have had flame throwers or chemical bombs in that Horse, it's just another dirty foreign trick but are we downhearted, the boys'll soon have this under control. The riot squad has been called out, O boy O boy what a bedtime story. There'll be an extra on the streets with all details, nobody knows yet what started the trouble but the fire is certainly a wonderful sight. The Hotel Ucalegon is burning right next door it looks like it might spread to Priam's Palace but the Junior League girls are out with their buckets, folks there's absolutely no cause for panic, they've just told me to advise everybody to keep off the streets. The editorial rooms are on fire but they don't think it will spread to the pressroom in the basement, folks I'll have to sign off for a few minutes while we check up. . . .

But there is no time now to explain how sorry we are, we didn't know this sort of thing was going to happen; and we scarcely heed Ilium's last words, for Troilus and the others he has gathered rush into the opening for the last attempt.

Greeks are in the archway, and among the foremost, Diomedes. Beautiful with glitter, accidents of light are on their bronze. The destiny is upon them, now The Wisdom is theirs for the instant, they are the dreaded meaning, the angry atoms of the world. They are color and measure and form, they are themselves the gods they invented. Nothing can hold them now. Troy had her chance. The engined Horse roars with science, it shines, spouts living fire.

The Trojans, though knowing it not, are happy to be so hopeless. Troilus is outlined in blaze. O ecstasy, for here is Diomedes. They know, and all men know, these are each other's. Troilus drives for the unplated breast, where the armor had been. Diomedes guards, and cleverly, but gets the blade through the throat: that throat of so confident words, the throat where the blue badge was worn. He tries to speak, and chokes, and falls.

It is not long. The Horse opens and vents its men. Achilles, Ulysses, Ajax, the ingenious Agamemnon, all are upon him. He is down. No lesser than Achilles deals the blessed stroke.

They pour through, to seek the citadel. Cassandra and Uncle Pan, in the wavering shadow and flame-light of the broken wall, raise him with cruel kindness.

Words are the last to die:—

Anyhow, we lit the bonfire, he whispers.

But the tall fury of burning Troy is too savage. It floods the gateway as did an eastern sun one morning. I'm sorry, (he tries to cover his face) it's too bright for my eyes.

XXVII

EPILOGUE—ETERNITY MARCHES ON

THE ELYSIAN FIELDS NEED NOT be described. Everyone knows what they look like: in one landscape all our glimpses of most perfect pleasure: when the sun dallied longest in the afternoon sky; when thought (the enemy of life) was abolished. In that unchanging beauty which is memory—and which first was beauty only because it always changed—the spirits we love have their own chosen form and purpose. There you may be old or young (or even middle-aged) as you prefer.

It looks just now rather like a college playing field; and that little stream, diminished so small and clear in shady windings, is really Ocean River. A new arrival is being shown around. This is done not because it's so different but because it's just the same; which is always hardest to realize.

She sees a group of white athletic figures practising the javelin and discus and the manual of arms. They are the Trojan and Greek officers, exercising together; in endless laughter, angers forgotten. One makes a beautiful spear-cast. High and long and level it flies, and there's brotherly applause. Another tries, and throws almost as far. There is very nearly the same approval. The group breaks and they separate into friendly discussion.

But a small ghost, darker than the others, isn't satisfied.

Like I said, he grumbles. Marse Trolius aint usin' de ole trapezius. He kin match Marse Achilles ef he really shove.

Priam agrees: The boys are a little soft.

Don' know how 'tis, King Basilisk, don' seem to be quite de same incense.

Incentive, Priam corrects him.

Yassuh, incentive. Dat's de big needful.

Shining and beautiful, a young shape comes forward, trailing his spear.

Marse Trolius, says Fuscus, you got to put mo' heft in it. You throw a mite fu'ther than Marse Diomedes but you aint really pushin'. Ef you don' feel competition, think some up.

Good old Fuscus, says Troilus. Easily he bends his weapon into a hoop and rolls it at his rival across the blue and golden sward. Both laugh.

Let's have a swim, Diomedes calls. Race you to the river!

They haven't noticed the newcomer, who is watching curiously. Perhaps pure and endless afternoon and infinite content dull the faculties: she seems puzzled.

Who were those boys, she asks the guide. There was something familiar about them?

THIS BOOK IS SET IN WALBAUM,
a type face originally cut by J. G. Justus Erich Walbaum.
Born 1768, the son of a clergyman, Walbaum became acquainted with forms and moulds while serving an apprenticeship in a confectionary. Later, after having perfected his skill as a form-cutter, he turned to cutting punches, matrices and tools for type-cutters. At the age of thirty, he married, and shortly thereafter established his own type foundry. In 1803, he moved from Goslar to Weimar, where he greatly enlarged his shop. In 1828, he transferred the business to his son who died in 1830. Walbaum then continued at the head of his foundry until 1838, at which time he sold everything to J. F. Brockhaus, printers in Leipzig. One year later, he died. His type faces enjoyed a great popularity during his life time.

The original punches remained in the possession of the firm of Brockhaus until 1919. Only a few years ago, the Intertype Corporation *made this beautiful type face available for machine composition.*

Together with the contemporary Didot *of Paris, and* Bodoni *of Parma, Walbaum of Weimar is the outstanding master of the type design we are accustomed to calling "modern."*

THIS BOOK WAS SET, PRINTED AND BOUND BY THE
AMERICAN BOOK BINDERY—STRATFORD PRESS, INC.
PAPER WAS MADE BY THE SCHUYLKILL PAPER CO.
TYPOGRAPHY AND COVER DESIGN BY ANDOR BRAUN